DEVON

To my friend Bob
memories fondly remembered
Best Wishes,
[illegible signature]
1/10/05

ALSO BY ARNIE WARREN

The Great Connection

The Great Connection Personal Action Guide

Find Your Passion

History of Chautauqua (Live Performance on DVD)

THE GREAT CONNECTION SEQUEL:

DEVON

Arnie Warren

Publisher's Note

This is a work of fiction. Names, characters, places, and incidents either are the product of the author's imagination or are used fictitiously, and any resemblance to actual persons, living or dead, events, or locales is entirely coincidental.

Published by:

Pallium Books

Plantation, FL 33317

E-mail: arniewarren@msn.com

Web site: www.greatconnection.com

Cover quote by Renae Tolbert

Library of Congress Control Number: 2004098129

ISBN 0-9655148-9-7

Printed in the United States of America

10 9 8 7 6 5 4 3 2

For Kathleen

Acknowledgements

My deep appreciation and thanks to friends who offered their expertise in creating Devon: Robert Lefton, Ph.D.; Russell Reinhard, Ph.D.; Robert Singal, M.D.; and Damian Roberti. A special thanks to those who offered comments and suggestions on the manuscript: Julie Conner, Alpha and Renae Tolbert, Sid Levin, and Rick Stamm. A special thank you to Linda Sacha whose candor and critical suggestions cannot be measured in words. And to Kathleen, my wife, for tirelessly listening to the story over and over again, for discussing for the umpteenth time this or that as though hearing it for the first time. Thank you for your patience, positive input and faith.

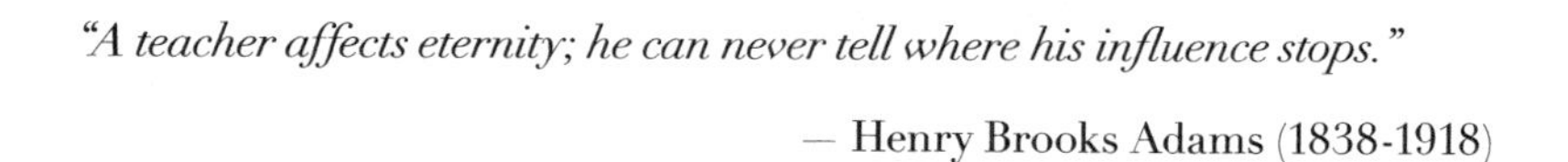

"A teacher affects eternity; he can never tell where his influence stops."

— Henry Brooks Adams (1838-1918)

"If you deliberately plan to be less than you are capable of becoming,
then I warn you that you'll be deeply unhappy for the rest of your life.
You will be evading your own capacities, your own possibilities."

— Abraham Maslow (1908-1970)

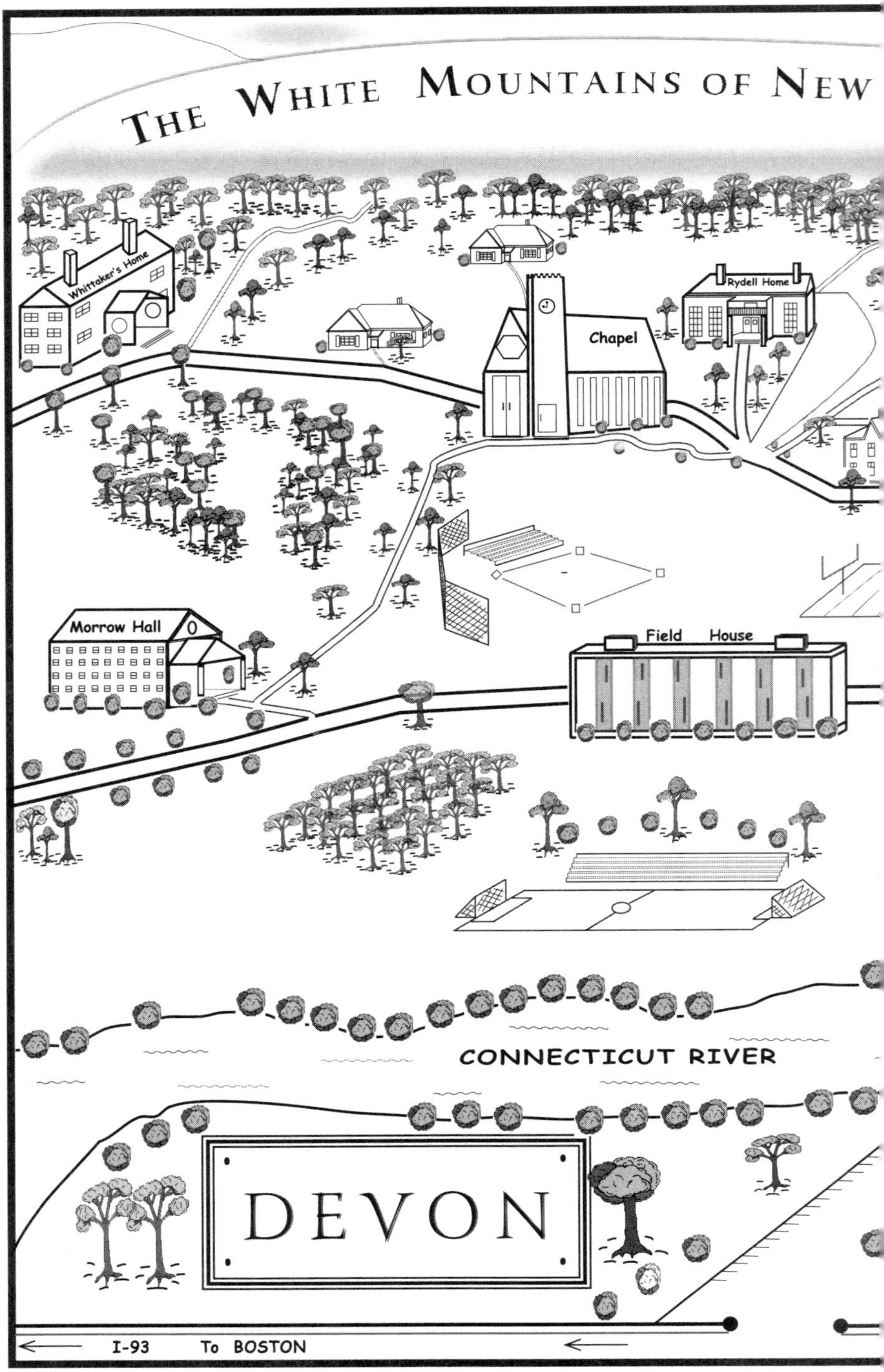

THE WHITE MOUNTAINS OF NEW

Whittaker's Home

Rydell Home

Chapel

Morrow Hall

Field House

CONNECTICUT RIVER

DEVON

I-93 To BOSTON

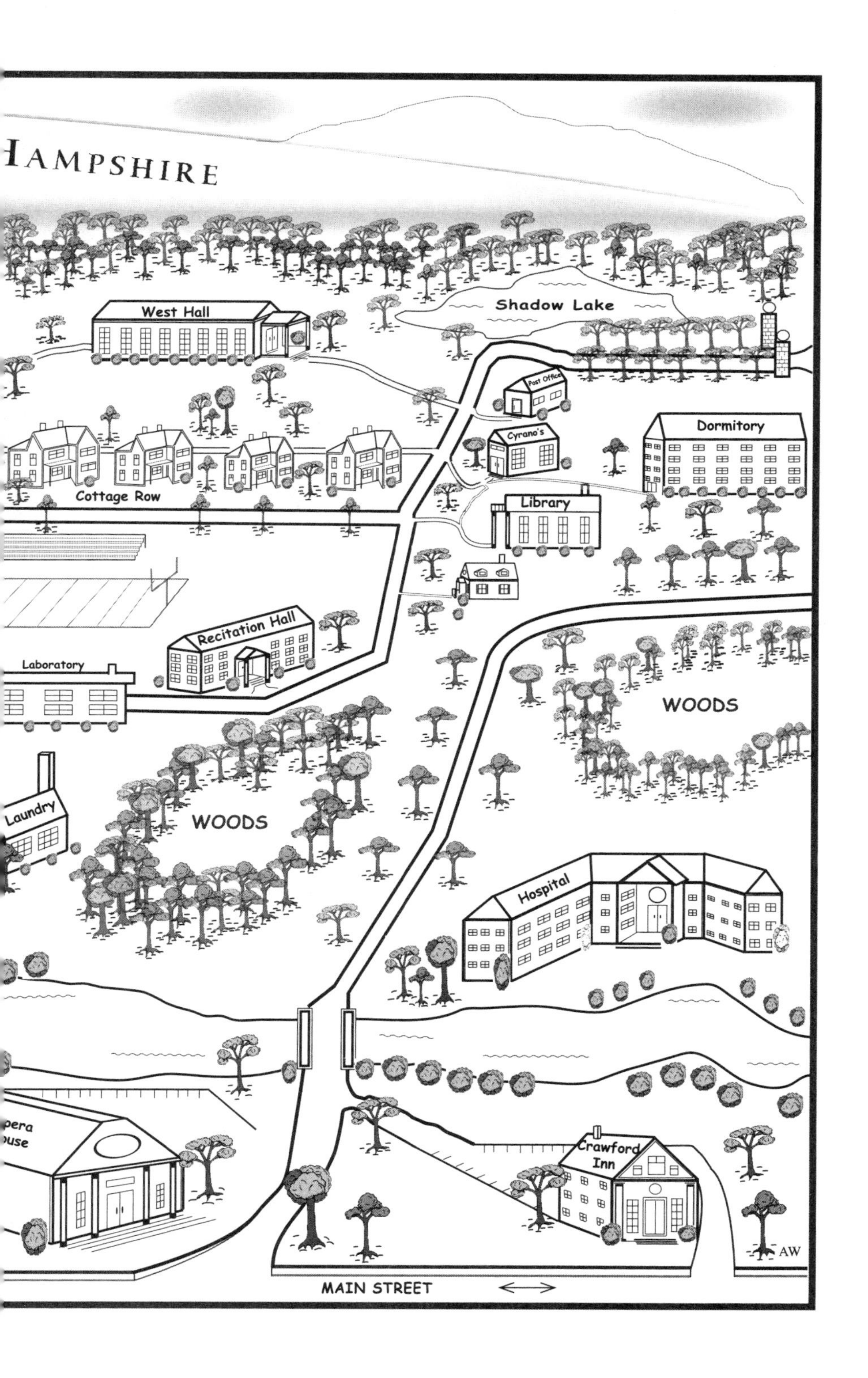
HAMPSHIRE
West Hall
Shadow Lake
Post Office
Cyrano's
Dormitory
Cottage Row
Library
Recitation Hall
Laboratory
WOODS
Laundry
WOODS
Hospital
pera
ouse
Crawford
Inn
AW
MAIN STREET

Monday

The Crawford Inn desk clerk fixed his eyes on him the moment he walked in. The gentleman set down his bag and placed his hands on the counter. "Registration for Hathaway?" The young man presented a sign-in registry card and placed a pen next to it, his eyes never leaving the indentation in the cheek of the new guest. The clerk would later describe it as how you look when you suck a thick shake through a straw. Hathaway completed the form and smiled at the young man. An embarrassed smile was returned. "Windy out isn't it?" said Mr. Hathaway.

"Cold front comin'. 'Bout to rain. Need help with your bags?"

"Please. They're in the Explorer out front. Can you park it for me?"

"Sure," he said looking at the registration. "You're from Florida?"

"Yes. Miami."

"Will you be stayin' with us long?"

"I'm not sure, but I'll let you know. Which way to my room?"

"Up the stairs and to your right. Enjoy your stay, Mr. Hathaway."

"Thank you."

Bob Hathaway went up the wide staircase and turned right at the landing. His room was at the end of the hall. He liked it immediately—a suite with east and west exposure, blue and white decor. He set his shoulder bag on the bed and crossed to the west window. Rain clouds were moving in, and the wind gusts sent the autumn leaves swirling in the parking lot below as he watched the young man tug his suitcases out of the SUV. His view took in the Connecticut River, then up the rise through a panoply of autumn foliage to the top of the hill crowned by the chapel of Devon Prep, the school he graduated from 46 years ago.

A knock on his door.

"Come in."

"Your bags, Mr. Hathaway, and your car keys." He held out the keys and stared.

Bob took them. "Thank you," he said pressing a tip into his palm.

"Thank you, sir."

Bob looked at his watch. His four thirty appointment with Headmaster Rydell left him one hour to shower and change.

His return to Devon began with an automobile accident that had shattered his cheek bone leaving a hollow contour. It was not ugly, but people couldn't control their stare when they saw him. That was enough for Bob to withdraw from his career as a professional speaker. He believed his appearance would distract from his message. For the next five years he struggled—lost for what to do and where to go. The turning point came when Dr. Rydell of Devon called him to head up an intensive four-year Speech curriculum; something no other school offered. Bob recalled the words of Devon's founder—Harlan T. Whittaker—*Use your talents for the benefit of others, make a difference in peoples' lives.* He accepted the offer and made a commitment to a cause greater than himself. By so doing he raised his self-esteem, was open to being with people again, felt more like his own man, and eagerly accepted the challenge of doing what he loved to do—teach. His cause would transcend any physical injury, and he knew in time his self-consciousness would abate.

As he exited the Inn the rain had started, the cold front had arrived. He hurried down the alley to his SUV and drove the short distance to the school and his appointment.

"Welcome, Bob," said Dr. Rydell, an executive word-rationer. "Want to talk with you, re-emphasize my concern of how poorly today's students express themselves." He stood at his desk while Bob sat. "Bothers me they can't utter a complete sentence. Everything's abstract. No structure. They say 'he goes', 'she goes'." He threw up his hands and faced the window. "What happened to 'he said', 'she said'?" He watched the rain pelt the window pane, a wrist on his hip, fingers fluttering in frustration.

Bob looked around the office. It reflected the granite of New England—heavy furniture, walls of books and certificates—a mirror of Lawrence Scott Rydell's rock solid force. Many thought his manner cold; others felt his directness energizing as he challenged you to admire him. Competing prep school headmasters viewed him as an imposing figure with a predilection for elegant Italian suits and a nose for the net worth of alumni widows. On the edge of his desk was an artifact with the curious inscription: Aut doce, aut disce, aut discede.

Rydell turned and faced Bob. "Let me reiterate why *you* were chosen. You're here because you've spoken to audiences all over the world. You're here because you're an alumnus—know these boys as well as you know yourself. You're here because today's youth needs to learn to stand up, articulate their thoughts, their ideas. Your pedigree makes you uniquely qualified to teach them this *essential* leadership tool."

"Especially starting in their formative years," said Bob rising, pleased at the confidence Dr. Rydell had in him. "Doctor Rydell, before my first class, I'd like to address the entire student body."

"The purpose being?" he said smoothing his tie.

"To introduce myself to them all at once, instead of them buzzing about the new guy with the funny face."

Rydell ignored the reference. "What would you talk about?"

"David and Goliath."

"They've heard that."

"This'll be different."

"Very well then," said Rydell coming around his desk. "Have Marge snap your picture on your way out. I'll get a flyer made up. She's got your paper work." They shook hands, but Rydell held his clasp and softened his tone. "You'll also be an Advisor." He paused. "Many of our professors have been cloistered here for decades. Living in a world of bricks and ivy. Help our students discover their uniqueness, how they can apply it in the *real* world." He swept his hand toward the window. "They don't have a clue."

"I understand," said Bob. Rydell turned abruptly and Bob said to his back, "I've had experience with this sort of—" The headmaster was already seated at his desk sorting papers.

"Dr. Rydell?" said Bob annoyed by his sudden shortness.

"I'm listening," said Rydell not looking up.

"I'm curious. This Latin inscription on your desk . . ."

"Inscribed on the wall at St. Paul's school in England. Pepys' time. Around 1650." He looked up. "Means, 'either teach, or study, or leave.'"

Bob picked up his employment packet from Marjorie, mentioned the flyer and photo, and in a flash she had a camera in her hands and snapped his picture before he could offer his good side. "That'll be fine and dandy," she bubbled returning the camera to its case.

Outside, Bob buttoned his raincoat, tucked Marge's packet inside and watched a bicyclist on the road below—the tail of her yellow raincoat twisting and dancing as she pumped against the wind and disappeared around the bend. He looked at the woods behind the Headmaster's office and decided he wanted to go there for its solitude; a place to reflect, a place to relish this new chapter in his life.

He pulled up his collar, held its points against his neck and walked quickly to a path at the edge of the woods: the cross-country trail he ran as a student. The pungent wet leaves and soaked wood made his nostrils flare as he approached the brook where he sat so many years ago. He tucked his raincoat beneath him and sat on a boulder and watched the water rush over the rocks. The yellow leaves high in the treetops protected him from the rain and provided a golden skylight. He embraced his legs and rested his chin on his knees and thought how Helen would have liked this. As soon as he thought of his wife, the replay of the tragic accident came over him. He rocked back and forth but could not shake it off.

They were driving home to Miami at two in the morning after his seminar in Charleston, South Carolina. They followed a semi, making good time through Georgia when the big rig swerved and began to weave. The driver over-corrected, the trailer flipped on its side and slid down the road in a shower of sparks. Its rear doors burst open and boxes tumbled out like rubber balls. Bob instinctively veered into the opposite lane before realizing a car was speeding toward him.

The grating impact remained a blur in his memory. He remembered his cheek felt mushy like papier-mâché. As the paramedics wheeled him on a gurney to the ambulance, he saw the other car buried deep into the passenger side of his car—the crushing reality. "Helen!" he had tried to shout, but all that came out was a visceral scream.

He dropped his hand limply in the icy brook and watched the water ride up his wrist and rush around. A chill went through him, and he withdrew his hand and dried it on a fold in his raincoat. A yellow leaf silently floated onto the water, and he watched it swirl in the eddies until the current carried it away. He looked beyond, deep into the woods at the still-life of wet, black trees until the dismal blur dissolved into an autumn day 50 years ago when the sun shone on a little boy soprano desperate to grow whiskers; his first day at Devon. He remembered the pain of prepubescence, of feeling more like the school's mascot than a Devon man that first year, but his mood brightened as he pictured his penultimate day: Senior Class Day.

The ceremonies were held outside between Cottage Row, where the freshmen lived, and West Hall, the dining hall. Wooden fold-up chairs for the parents were randomly set on the soft grass under comfortable maple trees and across from them, bleachers for the 150 graduates. Parents sipped pink punch and balanced butter cookies on white napkins while strolling and chatting with others whose commonality was the friendship of their sons. Bob sat at the end of the bleachers in the third tier furthest away from the podium where the class advisor, T. D. Donovan, an elfin man with black bushy eyebrows, welcomed the parents and began the ceremony to honor the exceptional graduates.

Bob looked at his Mom and Dad seated by a lovely maple directly across from him. He thought he might get the Choir Prize because the boys voted on it, and he was good at getting people to like him. He'd practiced for four years. And he did win it. He received his prize from T.D. Donovan at the podium and returned to his seat. He was glad for his beaming parents, but not particularly uplifted by the honor; it didn't compare to the achievements of the athletes or science wizards of his class.

A slight breeze caused Donovan to use both hands to hold the papers on his podium as he explained the meaning of the McAlister Awards. There were ten, he told them, each awarded to a senior whose over-all achievements transcended the norm. When the first winner was cited for being on the high honor roll for all four years, Bob yawned knowing he would not be chosen.

T.D. Donovan had presented seven of the ten awards—each

boy's achievements cited and followed by appropriate applause. Bob looked over at his Mom and Dad, and—in the split second it took to share a smile—his name was announced. T.D. read of Bob's place in the sun at Devon, his excellence in theater, his dedication to the traditions of the school, his generosity of spirit and talent. Bob's, his four years of personal challenges were swept away with these words of praise and appreciation. He had gained acceptance after all. Donovan placed the envelope into his hand, the hand of a Devon man who had transcended the norm.

He rose from the rock and walked back on the cross-country path, happy to be the newest member of the Devon faculty. It renewed his spirit, returned his optimism. He was eager to teach Speech to his young charges. Bob firmly believed in the rewards of being able to stand in front of an audience, speak to them, captivate them, encourage, persuade, inform—whatever the purpose. The rewards? Improved self-esteem, confidence, clarity of thought, making your point—there was much to share, and he knew the results would be fantastic. Plus, he had the honor and responsibility to be an advisor, just like a seminal figure in his life: Doc Crater. Without Doc's advice he wouldn't even be at Devon—would never have realized his true talent, his true gift, his *real* calling. And now he felt something he hadn't felt since the accident. Needed.

❑

David Viraldi entered New Hampshire's White Mountains on Interstate 93. He had arrived in Boston from Orlando, Florida at six o'clock, rented a car and headed north to Devon where he had been a star soccer player, an honor roll student and popular among his peers. But now, 10 years later, he was in a mild state of depression. His five-year marriage had ended in divorce, and his job selling time-shares in Orlando was shaky. He had trouble closing prospects because he believed he was selling something they would regret. So many had. His boss issued an ultimatum: sell or else.

He hoped someone at Devon could explain why he was a success then and a failure now. How did my life get so messed up? What am I doing wrong? He hoped someone could point him in the right direction. His spontaneous decision to return to Devon was triggered by a photograph in his recently arrived Alumni Magazine—a picture of a soccer player, captured in mid-air, making a scissors kick and sending the ball into an opponent's goal. He *was* that boy once.

He decided to have supper at Crawfords in Devon, then drive over to school where a guest room had been reserved for him at Whittaker's Home, the first building Harlan T. Whittaker built over a century ago. Today, it served several purposes: an outpatient facility, home to Ms. Trion who operated the facility and several guest rooms for visiting alumni. David wanted to spend every moment on campus. He passed the exit sign for Franconia. "Two more exits and I'm there."

❏

Bob walked into the nearly empty dining room at the Inn.

Most of the guests had dined and were taking their after dinner drinks in the tavern across the hall. Gladys Benson greeted him.

"First time here?" she asked leading him to a window table.

"Actually, my parents stayed here when I graduated from Devon. That was a long time ago, and now, I'm the new Speech teacher. My name is Bob Hathaway."

"I'm Gladys Benson. I'm the owner."

"I guess you know Dr. Rydell," he said taking the menu she offered.

"Who doesn't?

Bob was eager for someone to talk with. "Can you join me?"

"Sure. And I recommend the Salisbury steak for supper."

"Then that's what I'll have."

"Be right back," she said leaving to give the waitress his order.

Gladys returned with a glass of wine in each hand. "Celebrate your new position," she said, and they touched glasses. "Well, what's your take on Rydell?"

"Be brief and be gone."

"Well said," she laughed. "He's made quite a reputation for himself. I don't think everyone is in love with his style, but he's certainly filled up the treasury. Tell me, how does it feel seeing your old school again?"

"Like I was home. All my student days came back to me."

"Is there a Mrs. Hathaway?" She saw him stiffen and knew she had overstepped her bounds.

"There was once, Gladys," he said softly. "Auto accident. Five years ago. That's where . . ." he motioned to his cheek.

"I'm so sorry. I shouldn't have asked."

Bob looked out the window at the rain sweeping over Main Street. "Much change in the town?"

"A little. The town fathers try to keep Main Street the way it has always been. Some new stores here and there. The big doins was refurbishing the Opera House. Sears Foundation put up some big bucks for that. Did a complete overhaul."

"When was that place built?"

"1894, I believe. My mother went there to the Chautauqua when it came to town."

"Chautauqua played here?"

"You know about that?"

"Sure. Today's motivational speakers are modeled after the speakers of those days."

They both stared at the table for a moment.

"Have you ever been away from Devon, Gladys?"

"Of course. Don't we all have to leave to find what we left?"

Bob smiled at the remark.

"I went to Smith, became a bookkeeper, then an accountant in Boston and finally CFO at Saks 5th Avenue in New York City."

"Really," said Bob. "That's huge. What made you come back?"

"Home is home, Bob."

"I thought home was where the heart is."

Gladys smiled. "That's what I always thought, but it's not true. At least in my case. Where's home for you?"

"I grew up in Fall River, Massachusetts, but I've lived in Miami most of my life. I was a radio announcer there, then a stint in St. Louis before going out on the seminar circuit."

"Lot of traveling?"

"All over the world."

Their conversation stopped briefly while the waitress served his dinner.

"Looks good," he said. "Thank you."

The waitress smiled and backed away.

"Tell me, Gladys, what did your boss at Saks say when you told him you bought an Inn?"

"He said, 'How can you leave here to go change sheets for strangers'?"

❏

David Viraldi exited Interstate 93, drove past the school's entrance, down the hill and across the bridge to Main Street and into Crawfords parking lot. When he entered the Inn, a wind gust took the door out of his hand causing heads to turn in the tavern. He closed the door and headed for the dining room when the desk clerk called his name. "David? David Viraldi, right?"

It was his old classmate. "Son of a gun, Bernie Callahan."

"You remembered," said Bernie.

"Who could forget you," he said walking over to him. "Best mid-fielder at Devon."

"I've got a picture of the team hung in the office here. The year we beat Deerfield. Remember?"

"Yeah, that was some game."

"What brings you back, David?"

"Oh, just came back for a . . . to see the leaves change. You can feel fall in Florida, but you can't see it. I'm staying at Whittaker's."

"Well, hey, let's get together while you're here."

"Sure, Bern."

"Excuse me, Bob," said Gladys, and she went to see about the young man standing at the dining room entrance.

Bob watched her seat him and briefly chat. Returning she said, "He's an alum. Staying over at the school."

"When'll this rain stop?"

"Sometime tonight. Tomorrow there won't be a cloud in the sky, and the sun will shine all day. Will you miss the Miami sun?"

"I'll just have to get used to it," he said placing his napkin on the table.

"Introduce yourself to Jimmy in the Tavern, Bob. I'm going to turn in. Glad you're staying with us."

Bob went into the tavern and sat at the bar. He thought about the Opera House and couldn't get over the fact that the Chautauqua circuit stretched all the way to northern New Hampshire.

Leaving the tavern, he bumped into David Viraldi coming out of the dining room. They faced each other for an awkward moment. Bob turned quickly and David watched him go up the stairs.

In his room, Bob took the papers Marjorie had given him to fill out and spread them on the desk then promptly shuffled them back in a pile. He was not in the mood. After his shower he slipped under the covers and thought of the little things he would experience again like autumn leaves, snowy winters, cozy fireplaces, new friends. He was amazed at the boyish excitement he felt, and at my age, he thought. He turned on his side and scrunched up his pillow. Isn't it interesting that the more you do outside of yourself, the more you become satisfied within yourself.

❏

It was 10:30 p.m. when David drove between the two brick pillars at the entrance to Devon, along the winding road and around the bend to Whittaker's Home. There was a note on the door for David: *Don't ring the bell, just come in. Your room is at the end of the hall on the second floor. See you in the morning.* It was signed S.T. He noticed her bicycle covered by a yellow raincoat on the porch. Same bike she had when he was a student.

Walking down the hall to his room, he remembered when he was a patient with the flu back when Whittaker's Home had an infirmary. He and others tried all sorts of tricks to stretch their stay an extra day. David's had backfired. When Ms. Trion put the thermometer in his mouth, and left to do the same to others, David quickly took it and rubbed it hard on his blanket. The friction had the desired results, but he over achieved. Ms. Trion came back, removed his thermometer and, holding it up to the light said, "Hmm, one hundred and fifteen. Get up and get out!" But she smiled as she yanked his covers away.

He stood by the window in his room watching the rain, gentle now, fall by the streetlight. He turned away, climbed into bed and brought the crisp sheet and wool blanket to his chin. As he drifted off, he was 16 again playing soccer against Vermont Academy;

dribbling the ball down the field under the October sun, zigging, zagging, rattling it against an opponent's legs, waiting for the goalie to commit, then bang! into the back of the net. The crowd's roar, his teammates piling on, the joy bursting within him. Oh, to find that feeling again. That—*I'm on top of the world and can do anything*—feeling. He was certain he would find it; that someone here at Devon would untangle his life and give him direction.

Tuesday

The morning sun sparkled on Devon's centerpiece: the chapel. When founder Harlan T. Whittaker was questioned about a church being the school's focal point he replied, "Never hurt anybody."

Harlan T. Whittaker was a towering figure whose words inspired millions. Even late in life he was in demand speaking at winter Lyceum meetings in chilly auditoriums from Boston to Denver and in the summer on the Chautauqua circuit under the sweltering tents from Florida to Kansas. He uplifted audiences everywhere by the thunder of his voice, and he inspired young and old alike with the power of his message.

His fierce belief that education was the key to success called him to found a school in Devon, New Hampshire that offered a solid set of moral and spiritual values and a thorough examination of the liberal arts. He believed mind and spirit should be exercised.

In the early days, he'd drive his horse and carriage through the woodsy campus and stop whenever he saw a student. "What did you learn today, son?" The student would look up at the great man and sputter something, and Whittaker would say, "Remember you're a Devon man." He'd point in the direction of the Old Man of the Mountain, and, quoting Daniel Webster, "Never forget that God Almighty has hung out a sign to show that in New Hampshire, He makes men." Privately, the boys laughed at his maxim; little realizing those words would be a source of strength for the rest of their lives.

He was a strong believer that manual labor built character, so he created a work program whereby every student spent at least 90 minutes a day taking care of things at school: mowing, raking, sweeping and cleaning. If they did a poor job, their supervisor had them do it again till it was right. Headmaster Rydell agreed wholeheartedly with the work program concept. It *did* build character, and it saved the school money.

Whittaker created the school motto: *"Live as though you were to die tomorrow, study as though you were to live forever."* And, he created a symbol: a pitchfork with the outer tines removed. Each year the president of the senior class took this ceremonial object, festooned with ribbons of each graduating class, and handed it to the junior class president intoning: "Devon boys can eat soup with a one-tined fork." And for over 100 years, every student believed that.

Today, he might be disappointed at the role the chapel plays in the students' lives. The board of trustees, on the advice of Dr. Rydell, sanctioned turning the church into a meeting place. Rydell stood before them and explained, "Over the years, student body has become more diverse. Many religions represented.

Can't maintain the single denomination established by our founder. Can't make second class citizens of the followers of other religions." He concluded, "It's still a spiritual oasis for meditation and prayer, and we are still honoring and respecting a fundamental American tradition—the church as a meeting place."

❏

The sun dappled the walls of Bob Hathaway's room waking him, and he thought of the speech he would give to the students this evening; the sun awoke David Viraldi in Whittaker's Home, and he eagerly showered and dressed to talk with Ms. Trion over breakfast; and in Morrow Hall the sun shone on the frowning face of Teddy Garcia. Teddy was repeating his freshman year stigmatized with the label *un*classified Freshman. He rolled out of bed, went to the window, opened it wide and stuck his head out. Brisk. He wished he could fly away because today Professor Leon Grumitch would hand back his theme, and he dreaded the grade he'd get.

"Shut the window."

Teddy ignored his roommate.

"Shut the window, will ya?"

Teddy pushed the window down to an inch of the sill.

"You had to do *that*," said his roommate pulling the covers over his head.

Teddy smirked, grabbed his dop kit and towel and went down the hall to the bathroom. Several of the boys were showering, and a couple of them were shaving. Sean Fogarty was at the sink, face all foamy, a razor in his hand, and, as Teddy removed his pajamas and stepped into the shower, Fogarty sang his tiresome song.

"Hairless Teddy, hairless Teddy, has no hair, has no hair."

Sean had a full beard at age 13, a point of envy with Teddy. When Sean returned to his shaving, Teddy took a mouthful of cold water, stepped out of the shower, and spritzed it on Sean's back.

"Son of a buck," he snarled arching his back. "I'll get you for that." And before Teddy could duck back in the shower, Sean snapped his towel on his backside raising a red welt.

Teddy dressed and walked up the hill to his work assignment as waiter in West Hall. The dining hall was a marvelous brick building with no pillars or posts to obstruct the view of 500 boys and faculty seated at 70 tables of eight, served by 70 student waiters.

The students, in their chinos and white button down shirts, filed in and sat at their assigned tables. Ties were required at lunchtime, jackets for the evening meal. Headmaster Rydell believed in the correlation between dress and table manners.

The highlight at any meal was the waiter's charge from the kitchen. Two student waiters in starched white jackets with shiny buttons opened the brass-plated doors and stood at attention. Out came the five faculty waiters; boys who made an art form of carrying a tray balanced on three fingers only—no thumb, no palm—with the tray, high above their shoulders, moving forward and backward with their stride like lava in a lava lamp. They made a sharp turn in the center of the hall and glided to the faculty tables at the far end.

Seventy other waiters in board stiff white jackets filed out and headed for their respective tables. Those with less talent balanced their trays above their shoulder with three fingers and a thumb for stability. The not so gifted kept the tray on their shoulder and flat-palmed it. The neophytes rested the tray on their shoulder, flat-palmed with one hand and death-gripped the tray with the other hand. Teddy, thin and short, had to "two-hand" his and lean to one side to compensate for the weight of the food-laden tray. At his table Teddy swung the tray onto a fold up stand, and, before sitting down, handed the food to the table head, a senior whose presence assured civility. This morning's fare: family style bowls of Cream of Wheat and Corn Flakes, a pitcher of milk, and hot pineapple muffins.

Teddy was usually not included in the table talk. It wasn't that he was ignored; he just wasn't included. As an unclassified Freshman, he belonged neither to the class he entered with nor with the new freshman class. He focused on his pineapple muffin trying not to think of where he'd be within the hour. He dug out the pineapple bits with his fingers and sucked on them before eating the rest of the muffin.

After breakfast Teddy cleared the table, hung his jacket over the back of his chair, picked up his books and resignedly headed for Recitation Hall and English with Leon Grumitch, the man with the perpetual smile even when he flunked you. "You flunked, but you flunked high."

Students both loved and hated Leon Grumitch. They loved his storytelling and hated his grammar instruction. Leon had a gift for showing students the parallel between an author's life and his or her work. How Fitzgerald wrote quickie stories for magazines to keep up the life-style his wife, Zelda, demanded; how Jack London paid Sinclair Lewis for plot ideas. He peppered faculty get-togethers with these choice tidbits confident he would not be challenged until Headmaster Rydell, a Dickens fan, rendered Leon speechless at one faculty tea by asking if he used Dickens as an excellent example of semicolon use. He had hit a sore spot with the Professor who, while a marvelous teacher of Literature, could not transfer that gift to teaching the rules of grammar. Instead of explaining where the commas belonged, he huffed about the classroom scolding they weren't applying themselves. It was their fault they couldn't grasp the anatomy of a sentence.

Leon Grumitch held all the proper credentials: BA from Oberlin, Masters and Ph.D. at Yale graduating with a Phi Beta Kappa key, which he wore more as an appendage than a piece of jewelry. He rarely removed his blue and white herringbone sport coat, his shirt's collar button was always undone; consequently, his necktie was forever askew. His complexion was, as his wife Meredith called it, English Pink, which, as an ardent Anglophile, pleased him. The glow was the result of his proclivity to scrub his face with a harsh washcloth and oatmeal soap. Sadly, no matter how hard he tried to portray an English gentleman, his name remained Grumitch; and he would always use his hands to express himself.

He passed out the graded themes. Teddy stared at the note at the top of his: "See me after class." His eyes glazed looking at all the red correction marks and his grade, a fat 45!

"Garcia," Professor Grumitch called after dismissing the class, "bring a chair over here to my desk. Your grammar is atrocious, but I want to address something more serious. Your integrity. The assignment was to write about a personal experience."

"That's what I did, sir."

"I think not. How could you possibly—at your age—change a transmission on an automobile? I think you copied this idea from a magazine somewhere. Isn't that what you did?"

"Oh, no, sir. My Uncle has a garage, and he lets me help him do things . . ."

"There's a big difference between helping out and what you've written here. This is plagiarizing. Now, where did you get this?"

"I didn't get it anywhere."

"Don't compound the matter, son."

"I'm not. I did it. What I wrote, I did. I wrote it!" he yelled in his soprano voice, and he raced from the room leaving Professor Grumitch sputtering, "Come . . . you . . . you, Garcia you get back here."

Teddy ran to the apple orchard. He belly-flopped on the ground, hidden in the tall grass. "God, please get me out of here."

❑

"Good morning, young man," said Ms. Trion waiting for David Viraldi at the foot of the stairs. "Did you sleep well?"

"Like a log." He didn't know whether to shake her hand or give her a hug. She decided. A hug.

"I thought you'd be up early, so I waited. Have a seat in the sun porch, and I'll be right back with breakfast."

Such a kind woman, he thought, still trim, looking fine in her starched uniform, a black cloisonné with her initials in gold pinned to her collar. He was unaware that today was the anniversary of her husband's death and that she was struggling to keep her composure.

"So," said Ms. Trion presenting a wooden tray with coffee, toast, a butter tub and a saucer of strawberry jam, "what college did you go to after you graduated Devon?"

"Well, Ms. Trion . . ."

"David, please, call me Sandy."

"All right," he grinned. "I went to Cornell for their hotel school." He watched her eyebrows rise. "I love to cook, and I thought I'd end up working in a hotel. I did, you know, summers during college at a resort in Hampton Beach."

"I had no idea you fancied that. So, life's treating you well?"

"Not really," he sighed.

"Oh?"

"I'm divorced, and I think I'm going to lose my job. How's that for openers?"

"I'm sorry to hear that, David." Sandy Trion picked up some toast crumbs on the white table cloth with a roll of her index finger and thumbed them, rather elegantly David thought, over her plate. "Are you in the hotel business?"

"No. You see my wife, my ex-wife, thought I could make more money in sales. You know, big commissions so we could get a house and furniture fast. That's why I didn't apply for a job in a hotel or restaurant. They don't pay so well at the start."

"How long have you been in sales?"

"Nearly five years. Hate it."

"And you keep doing it?"

"Yes. Dumb isn't it? For the past year I've been selling time-shares."

"But you still haven't told me why you're here, David."

"I need some direction, someone to show me how come I was so successful at Devon and why I'm failing now." He looked at her expectantly.

"Magic? Is that what you're hoping for?"

"Sounds silly I guess."

"Oh, no. It doesn't sound silly, and I'm glad you told me. Have you talked with a counselor or somebody back in Florida?"

He shook his head.

"Then I'll be the first. I don't know if I'm much of an advisor, but I'm a great listener. Here, let me refill our coffees. Be right back." Sandy felt a wave of emotion coming over her and hurried to the kitchen. In moments she called from the doorway, "David, I can't talk with you now. Please forgive me."

David quickly got up. "What's wrong?" Her eyes were moist. "Are you all right?"

"I'll be all right. I need . . ." She pressed her fingers to her lips. "It's the anniversary of my husband's passing."

"Oh, Ms. Trion. I'm so sorry."

She extended her hand to him as they moved to the front door. Sandy opened it, and a flyer dropped down onto the porch. David picked it up. It announced Bob Hathaway would speak in the chapel tonight, and it showed his picture. Students and faculty were required to attend.

"Sandy, I saw this man last night at Crawfords," he said handing her the flyer.

"Oooh," she gasped.

She studied the picture of Bob Hathaway.

"Wanna go together?"

"I . . . I can't decide right now," she said her voice trembling.

"I'll check with you later," he said. "Will you be all right?"

She nodded, and David stepped off the porch and headed for the soccer fields below the apple orchard. Sandy closed the door, leaned against it for a moment, then carried the flyer to the dining room table and sat down. She put her head in her hands. It was eight years since Tom had passed away. Memories of their life together came like a slide show clicking from picture to picture to picture to picture. Their first date, first apartment, first, first, first, till the scene in the doctor's office and the dreadful diagnoses: cancer in his lymph. And the final scenes of their life together: refuge at Devon, taking care of him here in Whittaker's Home, holding his hand the moment he passed, the funeral, the grave, the emptiness.

After her mourning period, several single teachers came around, but she offered no encouragement. She didn't consciously think of spending the rest of her life alone, but it did seem the path she was on. Professor Grumitch's wife, Meredith, had nudged, "Wouldn't you like to meet so and so? I can arrange it. He'd be perfect for you." And Sandy would smile and shake her head, and Mrs. Grumitch would sigh.

During her younger years she always had a plan for her life. But the unexpected death of her husband changed her notion that life can be planned. "Whatever is in store for me, that's what will be." And now, as she looked out the window at the changing leaves, she said, "You have to go on, Sandy. You can't live in the past and hope about the future. It's time to start living. Now." She turned away from the window, dabbed her face with a napkin and scooted the flyer to her. She was attracted to that face in the picture and gently traced the hollow in Hathaway's face.

❑

Teddy stood at the window of his room in Morrow Hall and watched the boys down on the soccer field. It was 10:00 a.m. and he'd made a decision. Tonight he would run away to Boston. He had $48 dollars; money he had earned volunteering to mop the chapel floor.

With the money in his pocket, he left Morrow Hall for town. On Main Street, he walked directly to the variety store where he'd seen the bus schedule taped to the counter. The bus to Boston stopped in Devon at 7:30 p.m. arrived in Boston at 11:00 p.m. Perfect.

"How much to Boston?" he asked the clerk.

"Twenty nine dollars."

"I'll take one," he said, "and a Snicker's bar, too."

"You're at Devon?"

"Yes, I am," he replied handing him the money. "My parents were in an accident, and I have to get home. Sister called me an hour ago."

The clerk looked at him suspiciously.

"What'd ya think, I'm running away?"

The clerk counted his money and gave him his ticket. He

walked out of the store and down the street munching his candy bar, nervous about his undertaking, confident he could hook up with a garage in Boston, guilty about disappointing his mother.

His mother, Lyla, was the dominant figure in the family. His father, Pepe, had played trumpet in the house band at the San Souci nightclub in Havana in the early 1950s where he met and proposed to Lyla, a fiery-eyed sparrow of a woman who could sing *Besame Mucho* better than anyone he had ever heard.

When Fidel Castro closed the San Souci, Pepe formed a sextet featuring Lyla, but jobs were hard to come by. People didn't have money to spend. From the bandstand of the small clubs he played, he complained how Castro had taken away their freedom to make a decent living. Lyla warned him his mouth would get him in trouble, and he should be more careful as she was pregnant. He paid no heed, spoke more stridently and was arrested.

Word of his harsh treatment in prison got back to Lyla. Friends urged her to run away from Cuba, go to Miami, and she did. After Teddy's birth she learned English in the evening at the vocational school and studied to be a social worker. Now, she was the Director of the Little Havana Community Center on 8th street.

When Teddy was ten, his father was released from prison. This once energetic musician who cut such a commanding figure on stage was now a demoralized man who sat in their living room drifting in and out of reality.

Teddy's mother knew she had to get her young son out of this environment. It was her dream that he go to Devon because of the school's reputation and the financial aid they provided. She wanted him to amount to something, but her dream was his nightmare because all he wanted was to be a mechanic.

As Teddy walked up the hill to school, he rationalized that because his mother had run away when she was young she'd understand.

❑

After breakfast, Bob Hathaway walked outside Crawfords Inn. It was just as Gladys said—clear blue sky and bright sun, although it was chilly. He headed up Main Street to the Opera House. He was drawn to it. Had to walk on the stage where H. T. Whittaker and other orators of the late 19th century had paced.

He touched one of the columns as he climbed the granite steps. In the lobby, sets of double doors opened to the main floor. Bob entered and looked at the proscenium arch draped in green velvet with gold-fringe and the town seal hung in the center. The seal depicted the state with a star where Devon was located and the words, Chartered in 1784. In the background, the Connecticut River and the Old Man of the Mountain.

Bob walked down the aisle, vaulted onto the stage and looked out to the house and up at the horseshoe shaped balcony. He couldn't resist checking the acoustics. In all of his "sound checks" he recited part of a poem by Leigh Hunt he learned in the 7th grade.

Abou Ben Adhem, may his tribe increase awoke one night from a deep dream of peace and saw, within the moonlight of his room, making it rich, like a lily in bloom, an angel writing in a book of gold.

His deep and rumbly voice resonated throughout the hall as

he moved about the stage checking for dead spots. Acoustically, the Opera House was near perfect, and, since no one was around, he rehearsed the speech he would give tonight in the chapel.

❑

At mid-afternoon David Viraldi pawed through the rack of Devon warm up jackets in Cyrano's, the campus store and coffee shop. The jackets were shiny and silky to the touch, and the white Devon crest stood out nicely on the deep maroon of the jacket. White stripes ran the length of the sleeves and circled the collar and cuffs. He tried on a "large," and it fit perfectly. The cashier leaned across the counter and carefully snipped off the bar code tag so he wouldn't have to remove the jacket while he paid for it.

After buying an ice cream soda he looked for a table in the crowded coffee shop. The only available seat was at a table where a young man was flipping through a car magazine.

"May I join you?"

"Help yourself."

"My name is David Viraldi. I'm an alum."

"Teddy Garcia," said Teddy closing his magazine.

"*Motor Trend*?" asked David.

"Yep," he replied with a yawn.

"Wanna talk for a bit? Kinda nice to get to know you guys."

Teddy nodded.

"First time away from home?"

"No, I came here last year."

"So, you're a sophomore."

Teddy's lips tightened, and he frowned. "No, Mister Viraldi, I'm still a freshman. Worse actually. I'm an unclassified freshman."

"Bummer."

Teddy looked at his fingernails, decided one needed attention and gnawed on it. "What do you do, sir?"

"I'm a time-share salesman."

Teddy looked at him blankly. "What's that?"

"I sell people deluxe vacation apartments. The time-share aspect allows them to vacation in other apartments all over the world."

"And going to Devon got you that job?"

Before David could respond, Teddy fired another question. "Do you like doing that?"

"I hate it."

"Why do you stay if you hate it?"

David shrugged.

"What does ya wife say?"

"I'm divorced." Then he laughed. "Both our lives are on a roll, aren't they, Teddy?"

"Yeah. I'm an *un*classified freshman, you're an *un*classified adult."

The conversation stalled.

"Like cars do you?" said David nodding to the *Motor Trend.*

"Yep. I'm going to be a mechanic."

"How can you be so sure?"

"Just am."

David envied his edgy attitude. "How are your grades?"

"Don't ask."

"Is it because you've lost a little confidence after flunking your first year?"

"I haven't lost any confidence," he said flipping his cap around backwards. "I just don't like school."

"You're failing, yet you're confident?"

"Very. Just because I don't like school doesn't mean I'm unconfident . . . if that's a word."

"No, it's a condition."

"Aren't you confident?" Teddy asked.

David didn't expect the question and, "I used to be," came tumbling out of his mouth.

The confession made Teddy uncomfortable, and he rolled up his magazine. "Hey, it's been nice talking with you, Mister."

David could only nod, embarrassed that Teddy had a better grasp of his future than he did. He clanked his spoon to the bottom of his glass, pinned some ice cream to the side and slid it sloppily into his mouth. He checked the front of his Devon jacket to see if he'd dripped ice cream on it. He hadn't.

❑

At supper Teddy wolfed down some meatloaf, sneaked a couple of rolls in his pocket and, feigning he didn't feel well, asked another boy to clear the table. He ran to his dorm, threw his clothes into his book bag, and wrote a note for his roommate to tell the dorm advisor he was at the library. It was 7:20 p.m. when he arrived at the Opera House parking lot.

❑

Sandy Trion and David Viraldi walked to the chapel eager to hear Bob Hathaway speak. Sandy had changed from her nurse's uniform to a woolen dress with a muted multi-colored knitted vest that David thought made her look dowdy. He wore jeans, white shirt, tie and a blue blazer—same as when he was a student. They entered the chapel and climbed the stairs to the balcony where guests and faculty sat. They nodded to Professor Grumitch, who sat with his arms folded across his chest, and his wife Meredith, neat as a pin as always. Sandy stopped for a whispered chat with Meredith.

"Follow me," said Headmaster Rydell as he led Bob up the narrow staircase to the chancel. Bob sat in one of the three high backed throne chairs, a vestige of when the chapel served a higher calling. Dr. Rydell introduced him. He spoke of Bob's experience, his alumnus status, and new role as Speech teacher and Advisor. After the introduction, Bob took his place at the pulpit. It arched like a ship's outrigger. He studied each section of the audience including the balcony where faculty, Sandy Trion and David Viraldi sat.

"Good evening," he began in his rich, bass voice. "I want to tell you a story, the story of David and Goliath and the lesson in that story. David is the youngest of eight children. He helps tend sheep with his father. His brothers are in the army. War is brewing between the Israelites and the Philistines.

"David's father, Jesse, says to him, 'Take some bread and cheese to your brothers and join up'. David says, 'But aren't I too young to join?' Jesse says, 'If we lose the war, what difference will it make? Go.'

"So, David arrives at the camp, hands the food to his brothers and tells them he's going to join the army. They laugh. 'You're too small, too inexperienced, why you're not even a man yet.' David stood firm, 'Pa said to join up. Eat your cheese.'"

The students laughed. They enjoyed this storyteller with the soothing voice. In the balcony, David Viraldi was entertained; Sandy Trion, mesmerized.

"Suddenly, from the far hilltop, Goliath appears. He stands nine feet five inches tall. He's wearing a brass helmet, a coat of mail, brass shin plates and carries a humongous spear—the head of it alone weighs 315 pounds. The brothers dropped their cheese. Goliath says, 'Chose a man to fight me. If he wins, the Philistines will be your servants forever. If I win, you'll be our servants forever. Send me a man.'

"David asks his brother, 'What's the reward for knocking off Goliath?' His brother says, 'King Saul will give you treasure, his daughter's hand in marriage, and free housing.' They both agreed this was a good thing, but on this day no Israelite dared to answer Goliath.

"The following day, David walked around the campsite and looked into the dejected faces of the men. 'What's the matter with you?' he shouted. 'Is our destiny to let others choose how we live?' That stung the soldiers—that a kid would speak to them that way. 'Don't you have a cause?' The soldiers talked among themselves, then turned to David and shouted, 'We've found our cause. It's freedom!' And David said, 'Will you commit to that cause?' And one by one each soldier made a commitment to the cause of freedom, and their spirits rose.

"Well, the concept of committing to a cause spread like wild-fire, all the way back to King Saul who ordered, 'Send me this boy.'

"At their meeting, David told Saul he wanted to fight Goliath. Saul says, 'Have you had prior job experience?' And David says, 'One time when I was tending my father's sheep a lion and a bear came along and took a lamb. I went out and whacked the lion on the snoot, got his attention, then grabbed him by his beard and did him in, did the same thing to the bear. I got the lamb back.'

"Saul was impressed. David qualified. 'You've got the job,' he said. 'Now, let me show you how to dress for battle.' He had him put on a helmet and breastplate and gave him a sword. 'These will protect you.'

"David stumbled and clanged around awkwardly; the helmet narrowed his vision, the breastplate kept riding up, cutting into his chin and the sword felt heavy in his hand. 'No,' he said, 'I can't wear these. Let me show you what I'm best at.' And he pulled a slingshot from his pocket.

"Saul's jaw dropped, 'You're not serious. You actually believe you can beat Goliath *with that*?'

'Yes, sir. It's what I'm best prepared to use. You'll see.'

"Well, you know the rest," said Bob speaking matter of factly. "He stopped by a brook and picked up five smooth stones. Goliath and the Philistines laughed at the sight of this young boy looking up at them from the valley."

Bob picked up his pace and volume and used broad gestures.

"Goliath came roaring down the hill brandishing his spear with the Philistine army behind him. David placed a stone in the pocket of his slingshot, twirled it over his head a couple of times and let it fly. POW! He sunk that rock right in the middle of Goliath's forehead, and the giant crashed to the ground. The Israelites chanted, 'Freedom, freedom, freedom,' and chased the stunned Philistines into the next county.

"How many Davids are here tonight sitting in this chapel with a cause, a commitment, a course of action? Or are you like the soldiers waiting for someone to inspire you?"

He leaned forward on the pulpit sill and spoke slowly. "David grew up in a little town just like Devon. He was considered too small, too young, too inexperienced. You are more like him than you realize, but perhaps for one thing. David had a cause to slay Goliath, and he was committed to that cause, and succeeded because he was prepared to take action.

"Have you ever thought about your cause? Ever defined it? Ever dared dream it? Dreaming is good. It's how vision is born, and how goals are established. But you have to make a commitment and act on that commitment to fulfill your dream. What will you commit to doing for yourself? Is it training harder on the athletic field? Is it mastering the rules of grammar? Is it memorizing your theorems in Geometry? What is your Goliath? And how will you defeat it?

"Sons of Devon, choose your cause, commit to it and take action starting tonight!"

The students stared; Grumitch glared; Sandy marveled; David believed he had found his mentor as Bob walked down the pulpit steps to the chancel. Dr. Rydell rose and together they walked down the center aisle to the back of the chapel. The students stood as they passed, awed by this man with the beautiful voice and contoured face who had touched their souls and lit a flame in their hearts.

Sandy grabbed David's hand and rushed him from the balcony and down the stairs to meet Bob Hathaway.

Also, hurrying from the chapel, grasping his wife's upper arm, was Leon Grumitch scowling down the stairs to the exit.

"Leon, for goodness sake," said Meredith shaking his grasp. "What's the matter with you? Don't you want to meet him?"

Leon said nothing as they scurried outside to Cottage Row.

"Leon, what's come over you?"

"How could Rydell hire such a showboat," he growled.

Meredith stopped in her tracks and waited for him to stop and turn to her. "Showboat? How can you say such a thing. He was marvelous. He challenged them. And look how they took to him." She raised her eyebrows, "Has the little green man got you?"

"Stop it, Meredith. He's a show-off feeding sugar coated jabber to these kids. And all the theatrics—leaning way over, almost falling out of the pulpit. And that Sandy Trion falling all over herself to meet him."

Meredith smiled. "And what's the matter with that?"

"Come on, let's not stand here," he said. "The students are coming."

At the end of Cottage Row, they turned down the hill and

walked in silence to their bungalow: a little white house with shingled siding, gabled windows on the second floor and maroon shutters all around. It was, as Meredith had said when she first saw it, "Optime," Latin for Splendid. She loved using Latin in the vernacular to Leon's annoyance.

"Leon, won't you write him a little welcome note? It's only polite," she said as they entered the house.

"Write a note? If you're so in love with him, you write a note," he sputtered waving his arms. "Invite him over why don't you. You'll see. Hathaway is trouble. What's your Latin for that?"

Without missing a beat she said, "Turbidare," and walked to the kitchen. Leon, from the hallway, glared at her backside. "You'll see," he muttered. "You'll see the turbid-*ah*-rey that's coming."

❑

Teddy gave a sigh of relief when he saw the big headlights of the Concord Trailways bus sweep over the Opera House as it turned into the parking lot. He boarded and sat on the opposite side of traffic in case someone from the school drove by and saw him. There were 11 passengers on the bus. "We'll be off in ten minutes 'case there's latecomers," said the driver picking up a magazine. Teddy closed his eyes and waited. Finally, the driver stuffed his magazine by his seat, put the bus in gear, pulled away from the curb and headed toward I-93 for Boston. The stops along the way were Franconia, Lincoln, Plymouth, Tilton Junction, Concord, Manchester and finally, Boston.

At 9:30 p.m. the bus pulled into the Concord terminal, and the driver told the passengers there would be a 10-minute wait. He stepped out, sauntered in front of the bus and lit a cigarette—none of the passengers disembarked, a couple were asleep. It was quiet until a passenger boarded and walked to the back of the bus banging his suitcase on the seat backs. Teddy felt hungry and wished he'd brought more dinner rolls from school. He thought of going inside the terminal but decided to stay put.

A man rushed out of the terminal and talked excitedly to the bus driver. A flashing blue light streaked by Teddy's window, and he saw CONCORD POLICE in red letters on the side of the gray and dark blue car. The three men talked and walked toward the bus. The policeman boarded, stood for a moment looking at each passenger, then came straight down the aisle to Teddy. "Your name Teddy Garcia?"

Teddy looked up at him. "Yes."

"Well," he said putting his hand on Teddy's shoulder. "I'm afraid this is the end of your bus ride. Come with me."

Teddy grabbed his book bag and followed the policeman.

"This is John," he said nodding to the man from the terminal. "He'll take care of you till someone from your school gets here."

"Come with me," said John, and Teddy silently followed him into the terminal. "What's your name?"

"Teddy."

"You hungry, Teddy?" he said.

Teddy shrugged.

"We have crackers in the vending machine if you'd like."

Teddy heard the bus pull away. The policeman came back inside the terminal. "Listen, kid, trust me on this. You're a lot better off than you realize. I don't know why you ran away, but go back to school and deal with it like a man," he said poking Teddy in the chest with his index finger. The policeman puffed himself up to his full six foot three and left.

"It ain't the end of the world, kid," said John. "Now, what can I get you from the machine?"

"I'm not hungry."

"Not even a coke?"

"Nope. Did they say who's coming to pick me up?"

"Just said someone was on their way. Help yourself to the magazines over there, but don't even think about going outside. Are we clear on that?"

Teddy nodded. He had failed to run away. He'd be punished, he'd have to face Professor Grumitch, and the boys would laugh at him. His bravado was gone. His options gone. He plopped his 76-pound body in a seat without an ounce of will.

❑

Bob strolled into the tavern at Crawfords. Jimmy and Gladys were talking at the bar. Gladys looked up when he came in.

"The word is out, Bob. And the word is, you were *wonderful*," said Gladys coming over to him.

"Thank you. Some of the faculty came up afterwards and introduced themselves. I met Dr. Dowd. I think he said he's the chemistry teacher."

Gladys laughed. "You know what the kids call him?"

"No, what?"

"The mighty molecule. I'm surprised he spoke to you."

"He is a tiny man, isn't he?" said Bob. "I don't think he weighs more than a hundred pounds. Oh, and remember the young man last night in the dining room? The alumnus? He's coming over tomorrow morning for some counsel. Seems to be a little lost right now."

"Meet here in the tavern why don't you. People don't start coming in till the afternoon. So, who else did you meet?"

"I met a charming lady."

"And who would that be?" she asked with a twinkle in her eye.

"Sandy Trion."

"Ahhhh, Miss Sandy."

"What's that suppose to mean?"

"Nothing, other than every single prof has been trying to go out with her since her husband died. What'd she say?"

"She liked my talk."

"And . . ."

"And . . . that was that."

"Bob," she scolded. "Come on. Tell me more."

"Well, she's a very attractive woman."

"You've said that twice," she laughed.

"Well, she is."

"I know she is. Do you think you'll be seeing her again?"

"I think that's very possible, Gladys. Very possible."

A little after eleven, Bob's phone rang. It was Dr. Rydell.

"We've got a runaway, want you to pick him up."

"Sure. Where is he?"

"Bus terminal in Concord. That's out Interstate 93. 'Bout 90 miles down the road. Exit 14 and take a right."

"Where's the terminal?"

"Stickney Avenue near Loudon Road. I'll tell them you're coming. His name's Teddy Garcia. Good boy, a little immature. Don't know why he ran off. Call me when you find him."

Bob hung up the phone, dressed quickly and went down the stairs. Gladys was at the front desk.

"Couldn't sleep?"

"Student ran away, and I've got to pick him up in Concord."

❏

When Bob entered the terminal it was after one o'clock. The terminal normally closed at ten, but John stayed with Teddy.

"You from the school?" John asked.

Bob nodded and walked over to Teddy who was asleep with a car magazine in his lap opened to a schematic of an engine.

"Teddy?" he said softly.

Teddy opened his eyes. "You from Devon?"

"Yes," he smiled.

Teddy sucked a big breath and stood up, the magazine fell to the floor. He picked it up and looked at Bob's face. "Wow. What happened to you?"

"Auto accident. No big deal. You ready?"

"I guess."

"I'm Bob Hathaway," he said extending his hand.

"Teddy Garcia," said Teddy offering a limp handshake.

They headed for the door. Bob turned, "Thanks for looking after him."

"No problem. Take care of yourself, kid," John called.

Teddy waved to him. "Thanks."

As they pulled out of the terminal in Bob's Explorer, Teddy said, "Are you a new teacher or something at school?"

"Yes. Dr. Rydell has added Speech to the curriculum."

"And you're it?"

"Yes. I'm it," Bob smiled. "I'm also one of the advisors."

"Am I going to get kicked out?"

"I don't know. I wouldn't think so . . . unless you've been in trouble before. Have you?"

"Nope. First time."

"You'll be all right."

They went up the ramp, merged onto the Interstate and headed north to Devon.

"Want to stop for something to eat?"

"S'up to you," said Teddy.

"Going to Boston were you?"

"Yep."

Bob felt sorry for the little guy and decided to stop somewhere where he could talk to him and find out what was bothering him so much that he would take such drastic action. A truck stop was up ahead. Bob slowed and pulled into the parking lot.

"Let's have a big breakfast. Whatta you say."

"Okay."

They settled into a booth and pulled menus from the slot by the napkin holder. Bob was hungry. He hadn't eaten supper before his speech to the students. "I'm going to have two eggs over on a stack of pancakes with bacon on the side. How 'bout you, son?"

"Gonna have the same," said Teddy looking out the window at the semis pulling in and out of the warehouse bays across the street. Bob followed his gaze. The truckers entered the big yard, got their dock number, and backed into their assigned slot. There were 15 loading docks. An office was on the second floor in the center. A trucker pulled in and stopped his rig opposite the office. The driver honked his horn, stood on his running board and waved to the office. A window opened on the second floor, and a man stuck his hand out showing two fingers. Teddy saw that the second dock was vacant with semis being loaded on either side. They watched the driver get back into his cab. They could hear the engine rev, even inside the diner, and saw the plumes of diesel smoke puffing out the exhaust stack. The driver backed up, increased his speed—never let up—faster and faster—then turned hard and slipped that semi dead center into dock number two. 'Fsssssssshh!'

"Did you see that?" said Teddy. "He did it in one move. Never stopped. Did it perfectly!" He looked at Bob. "That was a-*maz*ing!"

"Teddy," said Bob leaning across the table, "we all do something that's . . . *amazing*."

Teddy sat back in his seat. The waitress came by with two glasses of water and took their order.

"What do you do that's amazing?" asked Bob.

Teddy laughed. "It sure isn't writing themes for old man Grumitch." He lined up his knife and spoon on the table. "I don't know if it's amazing, but I'm good at working on cars."

"Tell me about it," said Bob leaning forward.

Tears welled up in Teddy's eyes, and he threw himself to the back cushion of the booth. "I want to be with my Uncle in Miami working on cars. I hate it here."

"Why, son?"

"I can't write themes. I got a forty-five on my last theme with fragment, fragment, fragment written in red all over it. But that isn't why I ran away. I ran away because Grumitch accused me of something I didn't do."

Bob did not interrupt him.

"He gave us an assignment to write a theme on a personal experience. I wrote on how I pulled a transmission off a Chevy, laid all the pieces on a tarp, and, with the help of my Uncle, labeled 'em. Then I put it back together. Took me three days, but I did it. Grumitch said I didn't—that I got the story out of a magazine. Said I stole it! I didn't, Mr. Hathaway. Honest."

"Well, that's quite a story," said Bob passing the maple syrup across to him.

"It's true. I didn't steal it."

"Teddy, I didn't mean to imply you did. I believe you."

"Why do we have to write themes anyway?" asked Teddy.

Bob smiled. "So the reader knows what you mean. If you punctuate correctly, the reader interprets your message the way you want it interpreted." Bob paused. "How are the eggs?"

"They're fine."

They ate quietly and watched the truck activity over at the warehouse. Teddy added more syrup to his pancakes.

Bob asked, "What do you suppose will happen next, Teddy?"

"I'll have to see the Headmaster, and the guys'll get on me, as if they don't give me enough trouble. They're another reason I hate Devon."

"What do they do?"

"They make fun of my high voice. They imitate me. They get on me because I don't shave yet. That sort of thing. See, I'm an unclassified freshman. You know what that means? It means every time we go to chapel, every time we sit in the assembly hall—every friggin' place the whole school meets, I'm in the back. That means when the seniors file out and the juniors file out and the sophomores—they see me sitting there. Mr. Stupid. My old classmates dropped me. The new class, the class I tried to make friends with, ignores me. So, I'm nowhere.

"Is facing your friends your biggest fear?"

"No, I can deal with them. My biggest fear, if you want to know, is seeing Professor Grumitch again."

"You know you'll have to apologize to him for running out of his classroom."

Teddy sniffed.

"And he owes you an apology, too."

"Yeah, likely."

"You know the biggest thing you can do for Teddy Garcia?"

"What," said Teddy pushing a dripping forkful of pancakes in his mouth.

"Make a commitment to learn your grammar. Make that your cause."

"But Grumitch never shows us *how* it works."

Bob took a deep breath. "Teddy, I'm going to tell you something I've never told anyone. You know how old I was before I learned proper punctuation? Forty-six. I had an English teacher here at Devon, T.D. Donovan, who I loved. He advised me on so many personal things, but when it came to grammar, I just couldn't get it. He tried, I failed. After graduation I wanted to write to him to tell him how much his *personal* advice had meant to me. But, Teddy, I was afraid to write and thank him because I didn't know where to put the commas, and I didn't want to embarrass him or myself. For thirty years, Teddy, I wanted to write to him."

"So you never wrote him?"

"Yes, I finally did, but first I had to learn punctuation," he smiled. "My mother had been a school teacher. I asked her to show me when grammar is first taught and all the steps from the third grade through high school. I wanted to see where I missed it."

"And she taught you?"

"Yes. And you know what? It's not difficult. Some teachers make it difficult. They spend too much time on the vocabulary of grammar and not enough time demonstrating how each element is used. They're like mechanics who tell you the name of every part of a transmission, but not how the parts work together. Do you see?"

"I know what you mean. My uncle, when we took apart the

transmission, would hold up a gear or something, tell me its name and then explain what it did and why it was important. It was easy to learn that way." Teddy paused a moment. He liked the way Hathaway explained things. "Would you be my advisor? I mean can a student chose who they want?"

"What would you have me do?"

"Can you show me where to put the commas so I can pass my themes."

Bob looked out the window and thought of what Dr. Rydell had asked him to do: *advise* the students. But was helping Teddy with grammar advice or tutelage? Yet, Rydell had emphasized that he show them their uniqueness. Bob rationalized that Teddy must know how to communicate his thoughts in writing in order to express his uniqueness. "Yes, I'll be your advisor, Teddy." He reached across the table. "Let's shake on it."

Teddy wiped his hand on his pants and shook Bob's hand.

"Let's start right now," said Bob. He took out his pen and reached for a napkin. "I'm going to teach you to never, ever write a fragment again, Teddy. When you're driving a car, what do you press to make it go?"

"The accelerator."

"What makes it stop?"

"The brake."

"So, to drive a car, you need two things, right?"

Teddy nodded.

"A sentence has to have two things, too, a noun and a verb. If one is missing you've written a fragment. So . . .?"

"A sentence must have noun and a verb," he responded.

"If one of those is missing you've got a . . . ?"

"Fragment."

"You told me you labeled each part of the transmission you laid on the tarp. Those parts are nouns, Teddy. Anything you can name is a noun. Now, to make a sentence using one of those nouns you need to add a verb."

Teddy nodded.

"Give me a sentence using a noun from the tarp and give it action using a verb."

Teddy leaned forward. "A gear turns the driveshaft."

"What's the noun?"

"Gear."

"What's the verb?"

"Turns."

"What've you got?"

"A sentence."

"Why?"

"'Cause its got a brake and accelerator."

"Excellent," said Bob.

Teddy took a sip of water.

"Ready to go?" asked Bob.

Teddy nodded, and they left the diner.

On the way back to Devon, Teddy asked, "Did you teach somewhere before Devon?"

"I had my own business doing seminars and keynote speeches. A keynote sets the tone and theme of a business conference."

"You were on the stage?"

"In many countries."

"Before lots of people?"

"I think my largest audience was ten thousand."

Teddy whistled. "Wow! You're going to teach us to do *that*?"

"Going to try, son."

Teddy was excited—thrilled to be with this man who seemed to care about him.

Wednesday

"I was waiting for you," said Sandy Trion as David entered the sun porch.

"Good morning," he said arching his back in a stretch. "Wasn't he great last night?"

"Hm*mm*. I could listen to him read the phone book."

He sat down, poured coffee in his cup and reached for a piece of toast. "I felt he was talking to me directly. Like I was meant to hear his message."

"Oh, Gladys called, and your appointment with Mr. Hathaway has been moved up to ten instead of nine. He got in around four this morning." She said Mr. Hathaway went after a student who'd tried to run away."

"A student ran away?"

"That's what she said." She watched him spread marmalade

on his toast. "You know what I'm going to do? I'm going to invite the man over for tea, but I'd like you to be here, too. We'll make it a threesome."

"Great. When's the tea?"

"Perhaps tomorrow afternoon. That's silly, that's too—maybe day after tomorrow." She smiled and idly smoothed the tablecloth by her setting.

❑

It was quarter to ten when David walked into Crawfords Inn and saw Bob in the tavern reading the Devon Courier.

"Good morning, sir. Great speech."

"Glad you liked it. Want some coffee?"

"No, I'm fine, thanks. Your message about a cause last night? I don't know what mine is supposed to be. I thought you might be able to help me with that."

"I'll try," Bob said putting down the paper. "First, tell me a little about yourself."

David told him about his successful Devon days and his failures since. "My confidence is shot, and I just feel lost. I never felt this way when I was a student. What changed?"

"Ever hear about your intangible needs?"

David shook his head.

"A psychologist named Abraham Maslow listed them like rungs on a ladder. Starting at the bottom and working our way to the top they are security, social, self-esteem, independence and self-realization. As each one is satisfied, we're motivated to satisfy the next need until we're at the top."

"I understand."

"If you feel lost, as you do now, this ladder is an easy check list to find out *why* you feel the way you do. Let's take each need and apply it to when you were a student to see why you felt so confident then.

"You were *secure* at Devon—set schedule, stable environment, free of worry or danger, so your first need was satisfied. You blended well with the students, so your *social* need was fulfilled. You've told me that these were the best days of your life, that you felt you could do anything. You reeked self-confidence so your *self-esteem* need was satisfied. Am I right?"

"Exactly," said David.

"*Independence* is the next to last need on the ladder. Tell me how you satisfied that need as a student."

"You mean, was I in control over what I did?"

"Weren't you your own man?"

"I felt that way. Yes. So, in that sense, I was independent."

"The final rung is something Maslow called *self-realization.* Your self-realization need was fulfilled because you were successful doing what you loved to do."

David smiled. It all made sense.

"Let's look at your life now, starting with the top rung and going down. Are you self-realized?"

"Well, I'm not satisfied at all with my job, so, no."

"Independent?"

"I used to be."

"How about your self-esteem?"

"In the toilet."

"Social needs? Fulfilled in that area?"

"Sort of."

"Okay. Bottom rung. Do you feel secure?"

"No," he said. "I'm waiting for the axe to fall at work."

"What if you resigned?"

David sat up straight. "Resign?"

"Just asking," said Bob as he looked at his watch. It was after 11:00 a.m., and he had a luncheon meeting with Headmaster Rydell to discuss the Teddy episode.

"David, you said you were lost. Simply put, if your intangible needs are met, you will not be lost. We all have times in our life when we feel lost. But you know what? There is always someone out there—an advisor, a mentor—who will help you get back on track. It takes courage to look for that person, and your coming back to seek answers proves you are a very courageous man. I admire that. You also said you needed career direction—needed to find a cause that you can commit to. Well, tomorrow we'll find out what you're passionate about. Once we find that, you'll know your direction—your cause."

David's wide grin said it all.

❑

Bob walked along Cottage Row to the Headmaster's home

and office. He nodded to the passing students and listened to their buzz about Teddy. The whole campus knew he'd tried to run away, and that Mr. Hathaway brought him back.

"Did you bring the forms?" asked Marjorie when he entered the Headmaster's office.

"Sorry, Marge," he smiled. She looked disappointed for she was eager to read his curriculum vitae and things of a private nature. As the Headmaster's secretary she was privy to confidential information, and did love, "heaven help me," she'd say, to pass along a tidbit about this professor or that student to the wife of a faculty member in exchange for nothing more than being recognized as an important person in the school's pecking order.

"Right on time," boomed Rydell coming out of his office, shaking Bob's hand with vigor. "Appreciate the heads up this morning. Dining room's down the hall," he said walking briskly ahead of Bob.

They entered a cozy room. The circular maple table was set simply. Shrimp cocktails were perfectly centered on maroon rimmed plates. Rydell made an open palm gesture indicating where Bob should sit.

"How's Teddy?" asked Rydell squeezing a lemon slice over his shrimp.

"He'll be okay," Bob smiled.

"Why'd he leave?"

"Several reasons, but the trigger was something that happened in his English class."

Rydell snapped off the tail of his shrimp.

"Seems Teddy has flunked all his themes, doesn't understand

grammar, can't seem to get it, but this particular theme was to write about a personal experience. He wrote about changing a car's transmission. Grumitch, apparently, didn't believe he was capable of that and accused him of plagiarism."

"D'you believe Teddy?"

"Yes, I do."

The student waiter removed the shrimp cups and returned with iced tea and the entree: chicken potpie.

"Let me tell you something. When the acceptance committee met to go over prospective students, they rejected him—too immature. But he'd passed all his tests, and his mother desperately wanted him here because of circumstances at home. I persuaded the board to take a chance on him. I want him to succeed, Bob."

"He's plagued with the unclassified freshman label. He feels he doesn't belong to *any* class."

"I don't know who thought up that system, they must have been mean to the bone. Might just as well hand him a dunce cap. Tell the kid privately he's on academic probation, don't tell the world—especially his peers."

Bob realized Rydell, for all his brusqueness, had the school's best interest at heart and that included every single student.

"You know why I love this place, Bob? It's so democratic. When people hear the words prep school, they think of some ritzy-ditsy place not at all like Devon. You know how many boys receive financial aid from our endowment fund? More than fifty percent. Try that on your Andovers and Exeters. We look for potential in applicants from all over the world regardless of race, color and what have you. We don't care who your Daddy is and how much money you've got. Just give us a boy with promise."

Bob watched him stab the last pea of his chicken potpie.

Rydell leaned back from the table and took in a deep breath. "You spent time with Teddy. What do you think?"

"I didn't see him under the best of circumstances."

"I know, I know. What does your gut say about him?"

"Several things. He's got confidence and loves mechanics. He's got a spark. I see that in him. Right now he's deathly afraid he'll be kicked out. He's worried the kids'll rag him. But his chief worry is Grumitch."

"Go on," said Rydell.

"I told him he'd have to apologize to the Professor, and he almost died."

"You sure he changed that transmission?"

"Told me how he put all the parts on a tarp and labeled them, then put them all back together again. The kid loves cars. Works with his uncle in a repair shop in Miami during the summer."

"Did you just talk about cars?"

"I gave him a grammar lesson."

"A grammar lesson? At two in the morning?" Rydell laughed, "Oh, Hathaway, you're good. What'd you teach him?"

"Simple sentence. He told me his problem was fragments, which meant he didn't understand what a basic sentence was all about. So, we got that taken care of."

"Think he'll run away again?"

"No. If for no other reason he's afraid you'll tell his mother."

"Naw, I'll talk with him this afternoon. Reassure him." He

paused for a moment. "Sounds like you two have a rapport. Be his advisor, Bob."

"Already am. At his request."

Rydell pushed his chair away from the table. "Getting nice comments on your speech. Ready to start class next week?"

"Can't wait."

Lunch was over. At Marge's desk, Rydell stopped and told her to get Teddy over for a student conference this afternoon.

Bob said his good-byes.

"Don't forget your forms," Marjorie said innocently.

❏

Sandy Trion couldn't get Bob Hathaway out of her mind. She could still hear him challenging the students to make a personal commitment, to find their cause, and his voice stirred feelings she'd not had in many years. Maybe I'm being too forward, she thought. But before doubt overcame her, she wrote the invitation to tea, then had second thoughts. She called Meredith Grumitch to talk it over.

"Wasn't that speech something last night?"

"Are you calling about the speech or the speaker?"

Sandy laughed, "You see right through me don't you? The speaker of course. What do you think?"

"Well, Leon wasn't taken with him, but I thought he was wonderful. How about you?"

"Can't get him out of my mind. That voice—." She paused.

"I'm thinking of inviting him to tea."

"Good for you."

"Do you think he'll come?"

"Of course he will."

"Do you know anything about him?"

"No more than you."

"He's single isn't he?"

"That's the buzz."

"So you think a tea would be appropriate? I don't want to seem too forward."

"Sandy. Boil the water."

Sandy sealed the envelope and left Whittaker's Home on her bicycle for the post office. She passed the Headmaster's house and up ahead caught a glimpse of Bob Hathaway on Cottage Row. She rode up behind him and rang her bicycle bell, "Mr. Hathaway?"

Bob turned.

"We met last night after your speech."

"I remember. You're Sandy Trion," he smiled.

"I was on my way to mail this to you," she said.

Bob opened the invitation. "Why, yes, I'd love to."

"I've invited David Viraldi, too. That should make it fun," she said immediately regretting sounding like a schoolgirl.

"That'll be nice, Sandy."

He was attracted by her energy, the sparkle and joy in her eyes, her nose with its perfect plane.

They reconfirmed the time, two o'clock day after tomorrow, said their good byes, and Sandy peddled off toward the library.

As she coasted down the hill she realized she was going in the wrong direction. Too embarrassed to turn around, she stopped by the Grumitch house and sat under a tree to settle down. Before Bob Hathaway came into her life, she was comfortable living with old memories, but now she considered creating new ones.

❑

Teddy nervously twirled his cap in his lap watching Dr. Rydell push papers aside on his desk and wishing the meeting would be quick, and he'd know his fate.

With heavily measured words Rydell began. "Son, running away is serious business. Serious because you broke a commitment to your mother, to yourself, to Devon." Teddy gripped his cap tighter. "Now, I want you to tell me why you ran away. You're fifteen. What were you thinking? Tell me."

"Are you going to expel me?" Teddy blurted.

Rydell relaxed his body and leaned forward. "No, son, I'm not going to expel you, but I must have a reason why you did something so dishonorable. You see, running away from your problems dishonors you. Now, why did you do it?"

Fighting tears, Teddy struggled through his story. When he finished, Dr. Rydell turned his chair to the window. "Mr. Hathaway gave a talk last night to the entire student body. You would have benefited from it—had your name written all over it. He spoke of David and Goliath." He spun back to Teddy. "He said David rallied his troops to fight Goliath by asking them, 'What is your cause? What are you committed to?' Well, Teddy, what are you committed to?" He watched the boy turn his cap in his lap. "I understand Mr. Hathaway is your advisor. Listen to him. That's all Teddy."

Teddy rose and went to the door.

"Oh, and Teddy?"

"Yes, sir?"

"Your mother won't know about this."

Teddy felt a wave of relief. "Thank you, sir. Thank you very much." He reached for the door handle again.

"One more thing, son."

With the door half opened, he turned, "Sir?"

"You will apologize to Professor Grumitch."

Teddy screwed up his face. "But, sir. He's the reason—"

"Ted-*eeee*?" he boomed.

"Yes, sir." He closed the door and headed for Cyrano's in deep concentration contemplating his apology to Professor Grumitch.

Dr. Rydell buzzed Marjorie. "Marge, get Professor Grumitch over here.

❑

"Leon? Where are you?" she called from the kitchen window.

"I'm in the backyard." Leon Grumitch straightened up with an armful of fallen leaves from the pile he'd raked and deposited them into a large plastic barrel. "What do you want, Meredith?"

"Come in." And she shut the window.

Leon shook his head, leaned his rake against the tree and

plodded up the steps to the back door. "What is it?"

Meredith stood by the sink. "Headmaster wants to see you."

"Now?"

"Yes. The Cuban boy ran away."

Leon's body jerked.

"Relax, dear, he's back. But he told Headmaster you were the reason."

"That *I* was the reason? Who told you this?" he said sitting.

"Marjorie. Not ten minutes ago. The boy was in Headmaster's office, and they talked about how you called him a liar."

"I did no such thing, Meddie. The boy wrote a horrid theme on how he changed a transmission of an automobile. Please."

"Why didn't you tell me about this?"

Leon got up and washed his hands at the sink. His breathing was irregular as the impact of his actions built up in him.

"When did he run away?"

"Last night, and the new teacher, Hathaway, had to drive to Concord to fetch him. The boy was on his way to Boston. Can you imagine?"

Leon was not happy with this news. "So what am I suppose to do?" he said drying his hands on the red striped dishtowel.

Meredith took the towel from him, folded it and laid it on the counter. "Can you prove he didn't write it?"

"No. I don't know anything about transmissions to question him. For God's sake Meddie, he should be apologizing to me for running out of our conference."

"He's a kid. Don't you think what you did was damaging?"

"And if I let him get away with lying that's damaging, too. Think about that," he said walking to the foyer for his sport coat.

Meredith folded her arms and watched him go. Walking up the hill, Leon tried to imagine what Dr. Rydell would say to him. He was 65, and the headmaster could legitimately ask for his resignation. But where would he go if that happened? I'll lose everything, he thought, the house, everything. A terrible wave of insecurity came over him. Garcia playing the victim, conning Hathaway and Rydell. And Rydell, a glorified fund raiser with no appreciation for letters and particularly men of letters and specifically old men of letters. He wondered if Rydell was hired by the administration to clear out the old fogies and make room for young bucks eager to save the world at any salary.

Marge pressed the intercom button. "Professor Grumitch is here, Dr. Rydell."

"Send him in."

Professor Grumitch entered the headmaster's office. "Good to see you, Lawrence."

"Have a seat, Leon. Teddy Garcia tried to run away last night. Why do you suppose he did that?"

"Well, as you know, I did not recommend he be allowed to return during our acceptance meeting last June."

"I know all that. I want to know why he ran away."

"Oh, I can't opine on that," he said sitting straight in his chair. "No, no. I have no idea what possessed him to do that. If you recall I thought him too immature to be Devon material."

"Are you helping him to mature, Leon?"

"I think that's in Mother Nature's hands, don't you?"

"Leon, you know what I mean. Do you counsel with him?"

"I counsel all my students. You know that. Always have."

"He says he can't learn grammar from you."

"Did he tell you that?"

"Hathaway did."

"Hathaway?"

"He's the one who picked him up in Concord. They had a long talk. Kid didn't know what a simple sentence was."

Grumitch clenched the arms of his chair. "And Hathaway explained it to him I presume."

"As a matter of fact he did," said Rydell.

"Mister Hathaway seems to have a lot of time on his hands."

"His classes start next week, Leon. And for your information, I assigned him to be an advisor. He's doing his job, Professor."

Leon did not respond.

"What's the average grade of all your students' themes?"

"I'd, ah, have to check my grade book for—"

"Are they improving?"

"Well, yes . . . most are. In all the years I've been here, my students have always improved."

"Yes, you're at retirement age aren't you?"

Leon was stunned. "I'm 65 if that's what you mean, but I don't see what that has to do with anything especially in the teaching field. Why, a great many teachers teach well into their 70s—"

"Yes, well, I want to see their grades, including Garcia's." Rydell stood.

Rising, Professor Grumitch said, "You mean today?"

Rydell came around his desk and put his arm around the professor's shoulder and guided him to the door. "Tomorrow will be fine, Leon."

"Tomorrow then, Lawrence," he said, and walked stiffly passed Marjorie and pushed open the door with some force. He was convinced that Rydell had been looking for a reason to force him to retire, and this was it. The unknown was upon him, and he was fearful.

He was half way down the hill to home when he thought of Doc Dowd, the chemistry teacher. They were the same age and were hired at the same time. Maybe Rydell has threatened him, too. Leon headed for the Lab building.

Timothy Thomas Dowd, Ph.D., a short, delicate man with brown eyes that never looked directly at people, loved working in the laboratory where it was quiet save for the sound of something bubbling in a flask or the thin roar of a burner. Few outsiders cared to visit the lab because of the smell of chemicals, so he was comfortably alone most of the time.

His grade book was all he needed to discipline his classes. Any disruption was quelled by his simply raising the grade book and waving it in the air.

During class, Doc stood behind a long, wide lab table with the students before him in tiers. He rarely looked up at them. Most alumni remembered his first lecture: lab safety. Doc placed beakers and test tubes and breakable objects on the counter, and, holding up a bony index finger, he cautioned in his thin voice, "When in the lab, it's safety first. Always." He dragged the sleeve of his lab coat across the desk and, "Oops." Several beakers caught on his sleeve and crashed to the floor. The student's looked wide-eyed. "Always keep the instruments before you. Oops." Another beaker and several test tubes took their tumble. "Oops and Oops," and the table was cleared. Lecture over, point made.

New faculty members asked that since Doc Dowd was more or less antisocial, why was he comfortable in a class full of students? The answer was simple. They weren't his peers, his authority was unchallenged. Did he consider teaching his calling? No. Chemistry was his calling. He was a practical chemist, not a theoretician; therefore, his experiments resulted in something tangible. From these experiments he created exercises that were so instructive and demanded such honest study that the students received a solid education in Chemistry, and Doc, unwittingly, became known as a great teacher. A student favorite was making a small bar of soap.

Outside of the lab, he wore a dark brown or grey suit with a tie, shiny from fingering, pushed up to his frayed shirt collar. He lived alone in Cottage Two on Cottage Row. He was officially listed as a Dorm Advisor, but students seldom sought his advice. His apartment had a bedroom and living room with a tiny kitchen whose counter allowed space for a hotplate and toaster for those rare times when he didn't eat in West Hall.

Leon walked into the Laboratory Building and peeked into Doc's office. It was empty, but his suit jacket hung on a clothes tree, which led Leon to walk down the hall to the lab knowing Doc would be there. He paused outside the lab door peering through the clear glass. There was the little man in his knee length lab coat, measuring chemicals into a beaker and stirring with a glass rod. Leon looked at the room. The walls were bare except for a large, colorful periodic table. He rapped lightly on the glass, and Doc looked up and nodded. Leon entered and sat in one of the student seats in the first row in front of Doc.

"Might get a splatter," he said quietly, and Leon stood and went over to the window. "What are you making, Doc?"

"Just testing the new chemicals."

"Can you talk, Doc?"

"Certainly," he said nodding to the floor.

"Have you met the new man Hathaway?"

"Yes."

"And?"

Doc said nothing as he filled a beaker at the tap, then with his tweezers released the tiniest bit of sodium into the water. It flamed and fizzed and buzzed around the beaker. Doc made a tight lipped grin, while Leon watched without a clue or interest in what was transpiring.

"You heard his speech in chapel?"

"Yes, I was there," he said slowly stirring the mixture until the buzzing and fizzing stopped.

Leon looked out the window. "Quite a performance wouldn't you say?"

"Yes, indeedy," said Doc.

Leon sighed. "Ever think about retirement?"

"Oh, yes."

"Well, talk to me, Doc."

Doctor Dowd took off his glasses and polished them on a

nearby cloth. "Yes?"

"About retirement."

"I think I'll travel when I retire."

Leon's frustration grew with Doc's taciturnity. "Do you *want* to retire?"

"Heavens no."

"What if Rydell said you *had* to retire?"

Doc Dowd adjusted his glasses to his ears. "Why would he do that, Leon?"

"Doc, I'm going to be straight with you. We've known each other for a long time."

"More than thirty years."

"I have a feeling Rydell is greasing the wheels for our departure. I think he wants to rid Devon of people like us so he can hire younger teachers."

"Really. What makes you think that?"

"A feeling. Wondered if you felt the same way?"

Doc came around from his lab table and walked up to the students' desks and took a seat in the last row. Leon turned from the window and sat in the first row.

"Was there something specific?" asked Doc.

"He wanted to know how I grade my students . . . wants to see their themes, and . . . there's other stuff, too," he added under his breath. "Is this anyway to treat someone who's given his life to this school?" Leon leaned in Dowd's direction and spoke in a more confidential tone. "He told me I was of retirement age. Actually said that, Doc. Has he approached you about retiring?"

Doc brought his lab coat over his knees with his tiny, scaly, liver spotted hands. "He asked me two days ago where I would live in my retirement."

"There. See that?" said Leon jumping up. "We're on the way out. Don't you get it, Doc? Our days are numbered. We've got to do something."

Doc stared at the periodic table. Retirement was always a far off dream for him; something that would happen years from now. The realization that the years from now were here hit him in the pit of his stomach. "Leon, he wouldn't do this at the start of the school year would he?"

"Who knows? If he's got a replacement . . ."

"I see." Doc didn't doubt Leon's supposition for surely he and Meredith discussed it. "What are you thinking of doing?"

"I don't know. This has come so quickly. I just don't know. I'm not prepared to retire."

They both sat in silence; the only sound a drip from the tap plopping on the metal sink.

"Doc," said Leon standing, "let me know if you hear any more of this from him." He left for home.

Doc sat there for 15 minutes before rising. He walked to the window, placed his hands on the sill and looked out. He couldn't imagine living in a place that didn't have this view, couldn't imagine leaving his little room in Cottage Two, of not eating in West Hall or hearing Christmas Vespers in chapel. He couldn't imagine being anywhere but here even though he thought of a retirement of travel. He shook his head. Traveling was only a fantasy. He would never be comfortable packed in an airplane next to a total stranger. He wouldn't be comfortable in the crush of a tour group. He wouldn't be comfortable not knowing what was around the next turn. He could never lie on a sun deck at an Alpine resort. He wouldn't be comfortable in a city hotel with its hustle and bustle or in the country at a pension crowded with backpackers and hikers. Where would I be comfortable? he asked himself. And the answer was Devon: safe, secure, predictable; among people who were used to him and he to them. His universe was Devon, chemistry his passion, routine his solace, teaching his reason for being. Devon was his life. Would Rydell take his *life* away from him? And in his practical way, Doc Dowd thought of options.

❏

Bob Hathaway entered Cyrano's, got a cup of coffee and took it to a little table in the corner, the better to hear what the boys talked about and how they interacted. The pace of his life was a whirlwind compared to how he had been living after the accident. Why, in just 36 hours he'd been hired, made new friends, spoken to the student body, rescued a runaway student, coached an alum, and had an invitation to tea, of all things, with a lovely lady. He saw Teddy sitting at a table in the back, so he got up and went over to him. "Want some company?" asked Bob.

"Sure, Mr. Hathaway. I had my talk with Headmaster."

"And?"

"Well, like you said, I have to apologize to Professor Grumitch. I'm still going to hear him say, 'You flunked, but you flunked high.'" He was momentarily distracted by some boys pointing over to their table.

"Never mind them, Teddy. You're your own man. Let's focus on your writing. We've already solved the fragment situation."

"Noun and verb. Brake and accelerator. Simple."

"Okay, what other things do you have trouble with?"

"Commas. I don't know where to put them.

"How many parts in a car, Teddy?"

"Hundreds."

"Well, in a sentence there are less than five types of commas to deal with. Think you can handle that?"

"Yes," he said flatly. He didn't really want to sit and learn about commas, but he had made the commitment to himself.

Bob pulled out a napkin from the container and passed it to Teddy. "Here's your first comma rule. Write down this word, *Introducer.* Now, write this sentence. *When the car ran out of gas Teddy walked home.*" Bob waited patiently while Teddy wrote. "Here's the trick. Look for the simple sentence, and the Introducer is obvious."

Teddy studied the napkin and looked up blankly.

"Talk to me. What's the simple sentence?"

"*Teddy walked home.*"

"What's left?"

"The Introducer."

"Where is it?"

"At the beginning of the sentence?"

"That's why it is called an Introducer, and it's always followed by a comma," Bob said. "So, what's the Introducer?"

Teddy smiled. "*When the car ran out of gas.*""

"Perfect. Now, go over to the magazine rack and pick one."

He came back with a *Car and Driver* but was frowning.

"What's the matter?"

"Pointing to the napkin he said, "Isn't *the car ran out of gas* a simple sentence, too?"

"You're right. An Introducer can be a phrase or a sentence, but the point is, it's *used* as an Introducer."

"I get it."

"Now, go through that magazine and circle every Introducer you can find. Your job is to find where the Introducer ends and the simple sentence begins. Note the comma after the Introducer."

"Will do," he smiled. "Thanks for the magazine."

❑

Sandy Trion stood on a booster step and reached deep into her kitchen cabinet for the china tea service. It was a beautiful blue design she had purchased in Boston. "Now, what shall I bake to go with the tea? I wonder if he likes sweets? I'll bake some scones, and he can put strawberry jam on them if they're not sweet enough. She opened her *Fanny Farmer Cook Book.* Should she bake the cream scones or Sharon's buttermilk currant scones? The latter sounded delicious; they had orange and cinnamon in them, but the cream scones were more traditional.

"Ms. Trion?"

"I'm in the kitchen, David. Come on back," she said.

David's cheeks were flushed from playing soccer. "I ran all

the way back, need some water."

"Help yourself. Glasses are in the cupboard over the sink."

"What're you making?"

"Scones. Cream scones for tomorrow's tea," she said wiping her hands on her apron.

"Great. Can I help?"

"You can watch."

"Let me butter the cookie sheet. Where's your cookie sheet."

"We're not using butter, David, Crisco will do."

"Trust me, just a little butter will make them taste richer. Use the Crisco for browning the top."

"Well, I guess that wouldn't hurt. Go ahead. The sheet is in the cabinet to the left of the stove." She was working the four tablespoons of butter and the other dry ingredients with a wooden spoon in a large bowl when the phone rang. She picked it up in the alcove between the kitchen and the living room. "Hello?" She listened for a moment. "Yes, he's here. Hold on please. David," she called, "it's for you."

There was only one person who knew his whereabouts: his boss in Orlando. He took a deep breath and tried to think of a reason why he wasn't at work. "Hello, this is David." He listened nodding his head. After about 30 seconds he said, "Do I have any options?" He twisted the phone cord in his fingers. "I understand. Could you tell me what my final check is—hello? Hello?" He put down the receiver and came back to the kitchen.

"I just got fired," he said, "over the phone. Boss even hung up on me." He sat down at the kitchen table and fiddled with the salt and pepper shakers, lining them up sideways then front and back.

Sandy sat down across from him and reached for his hands. "David, this is probably the best thing that's ever happened to you. You're rid of the job you hate. I believe there's a grand plan out there for each of us, and I think your meeting Mr. Hathaway is part of *your* grand plan. Your opportunity is right around the corner. Let's celebrate," she said. "How 'bout a beer?" She went to the fridge and pulled out two bottles and handed them to him. As he poured the beer into the glasses, Sandy said, "No matter what you end up doing, David, remember this. You'll never let yourself down. Most people don't know that, but it's true. When the chips are down and your back is against the wall, remember that you'll never let yourself down. *Know* that and go forward without fear." She raised her glass. "To your new beginning."

❏

Bob Hathaway stood by his bedroom window. The night was clear, no city lights to compromise the stars. He looked over to the school. There was the glow of the chapel clock and a single light coming from one of the cottages. He couldn't tell which.

Thursday

When Bob Hathaway came down the stairs to the Crawfords Inn lobby, David was already waiting for him. "Well, aren't you the early bird."

"Lost my job yesterday."

"You don't look like someone who's just lost their job."

David beamed, "Ms. Trion and I cracked a couple of beers and celebrated my freedom."

"Quite a woman, isn't she? Let's grab some coffee, and we'll work in the tavern."

Bob got right down to business. "It's good you don't have the pressure of getting back to Orlando. Just think, David, now you can do anything you want to do."

"If I only knew *what*," he said.

"Well, let's find out. I want you to tell me about three things in your life—your entire life—that you loved doing."

"You mean jobs?"

"Not necessarily. Take your time, think back."

"I loved playing soccer and being in the plays in college." He concentrated harder. "But I guess what I loved best of all was working summers at a hotel-restaurant in Hampton Beach. For two summers I was the assistant cook. The third summer I was the *only* cook. I made breakfast and a Friday night buffet for the public and cooked three meals a day for the staff of fifteen. I mean, I loved it so much I majored in hotel administration at Cornell."

"Let's find the common thread. What did you love about soccer?"

"I loved the anticipation of where the players would be when you're dribbling the ball. When you're out there, you can see the patterns develop. It's like chess. Magic when it all comes together."

"And the plays at college?"

"In college I thought I wanted to be an actor, yet the applause meant nothing, but I did enjoy delving into the psychology of the character. I enjoyed most how the director blocked us in scenes, you know, the nuts and bolts of putting a production together. I enjoyed the rehearsals more than the actual performance."

"Like soccer, you enjoyed the process of putting it all together. And working in the restaurant?"

David smiled. "Same thing. I love making things. Putting a meal together—the planning, the baking or whatever." He paused. "Mr. Hathaway, I love just *being* in a kitchen. There's something about it that attracts me."

"What was your favorite thing to make?"

"You'll laugh. Sandwiches. Can you believe that?"

"Putting it all together."

"Yes, even a dinky sandwich. I never thought of it that way."

Bob smiled. "So, why did you opt for selling time-shares?"

"Fast money, easy money, I thought."

"What did you first like about selling time-shares?"

"The presentation. It fascinated me."

"Specifically?"

"The sales pitch to get the prospect to say 'yes'." He paused. "Interesting. I love the make-up of things and what it takes to bring it all together."

"So, how could you leave your true love behind?"

"I guess being married, money was the priority."

"I don't think it was money. I think you're hiding behind that answer. What are you hiding?"

"Hiding?" David was surprised. "If I'm hiding something, I don't know what it is."

"I think you do. Talk it out. Tell me what it is."

David looked down and sheepishly said, "Low rent."

"I'm sorry?"

"I didn't take a job cooking in a restaurant because I thought I should aspire to something more . . ."

"More grand?"

"Yes, more grand." He gave a sigh. "I'm suppose to be able to eat soup with a one-tined fork because of my great education. What good is it if all I'm doing is making French fries?"

"Formal education has nothing to do with your passion. Formal education is its own reward. Gives you a richer intellectual life.

Maybe even makes you a more interesting person to be around. True, it is a prerequisite for some professions, but, again, it has nothing in and of itself to do with what you chose to do in life. Dipping fries in a Fryolater is not low rent if you love it. Look what you did to yourself. Look how miserable you've made yourself. You didn't follow your heart. Instead, you yielded to what someone else—including you—*thought* you should be doing."

"So, you think I should be in the food business?"

"I think you should do what you *love* doing. Isn't that why you chose the major you did in college?" asked Bob with a hint of exasperation. "Let's review. Your gift is a knack for putting things together. You are drawn to the food business. You are fulfilled when people have benefited from the results of your efforts."

David nodded matter of factly.

Bob caught the shrug. "You know what the hardest part of this is, David? *Accepting* your gift. We don't appreciate it because it comes so easily to us. Accept it, revel in it, be proud of it. It's your gift that'll take you right up Maslow's ladder to self-realization. You came here looking for a direction in your life. You said you lost what you once had. But, David, you never lost yourself, you just lost your way."

David brightened. "Does it always take someone else to tell us what we're good at?"

"Perhaps. Maybe it's so easy we don't think abut it. It's nothing special to us. Or maybe we *do* know and are afraid to take action. You've got to listen to the little voice inside you, David."

Their meeting over, David drove back to Devon, eager to tell Ms. Trion he'd found his focus. He felt settled, comforted by

Hathaway's words: *'You didn't lose yourself, you just lost your way.'*

❑

Bob was in the post office renting a mailbox from Mr. Willis, the postmaster, who still wore the long ponytail from when he played guitar in a rock band 40 years ago. A recluse by nature, he was happily at home in the one room, one-man post office. Between riding his motorcycle and seeing the boys every day he always felt young, and the bars on the window secured his space.

"I'll take care of it, Mr. Hathaway," he said with a stubby pencil in his hand. Bob was surrounded by students passing in and out, checking their mail, hoping for a package from home with cookies and such. They talked loudly about the weekend game with Kimball-Union, the tests they passed or failed, and some horseplay went on, too. Teddy walked in. "I've got something to show you, Mr. Hathaway," he said holding up his *Car and Driver.*

"Let's go outside," said Bob.

They walked along the road in front of Cottage Row, and half way down the hill to the football bleachers.

"What've you got?" said Bob.

Teddy opened the magazine to his first Introducer.

'According to AMG engineers, this results in a 25 percent reduction in intake-air temperature at full load.' Teddy had circled the Introducer. In page after page, Teddy had circled the Introductory elements.

"Well done, Teddy," he said.

Teddy gave him a smug smile. "What's next?"

"Interrupters. Technically they are called Appositives and

Parentheticals; one says more about the subject, the other is simply an aside. They are bracketed by commas. But what they *do* is interrupt the sentence. Hand me your magazine." Teddy did, and Bob thumbed through the articles looking for examples.

"Here's one. *'Chris Theodore, Ford's VP of advance product creation, summed it up nicely.'* See the Interrupter?"

Teddy circled the Interrupter. *Ford's VP of advance product creation.* "Tells more about Chris Theodore," he said.

"Here's another," said Bob. *'It seemed the Modena, sweet though it is, might not be a match for Ford's new supercar.'* He ran his finger across, *sweet though it is.* "See Teddy, this one is like whispering in the reader's ear.

"Remember, commas before and after Interrupters. Go through the magazine again and highlight the Interrupters and think about whether they tell more about the subject or if they're a whisper in the reader's ear."

"Interrupters. Like little islands in the sentence," said Teddy.

Friday

Leon Grumitch sat at the dining room table with his grade book. He wanted to get his report to Dr. Rydell immediately—he wanted to prove to Rydell that he was an exceptional teacher and deserved to remain Head of the English Department. His position was secure under the previous Headmaster, but now he wasn't so sure. Rydell was younger, had new ideas, new plans, and Professor Grumitch feared he might not be included in those plans. He was jealous that Hathaway had become the talk of the campus and had tutored the Garcia boy. He put his pen aside and looked over at Meredith sitting in the living room reading. She was his ideal.

Deep down, Leon was a very sensitive and insecure man. He grew up in Elizabeth, New Jersey, the son of Estelle and Vladimir Grumitch. Vladimir, a stocky man with a thick neck, short muscular arms and powerful legs, peddled vegetables from a converted school bus. That embarrassed Leon.

The Grumitchs were not openly affectionate. Leon felt one of three, not the son of two; consequently, he had little love for himself and what he was: Slavic. He wished he were English.

When he enrolled at Boston University, he wanted to fit in, so he bought button down shirts, regimental ties, chinos and penny loafers. But the Ivy League look was lost on him. The heels of his loafers wore down quickly under his weight, his chinos fit too tightly around his thighs, and his tie never set crisply at his damp collar.

In the first year at B.U. all students took an introductory class in English. In this class was a tall woman. Her name was Meredith Garlinghouse, and Leon fell in love with her. She was everything he wasn't. She walked on this earth as though she owned it; he walked on this earth ingratiatingly trying to belong. He adored her, but never believed she'd give him a second look. Apparently, the planets were favorably disposed because she liked him. She liked him because he loved literature, and she was passionate about the origin of words.

Right now, Leon needed her more than ever. He believed Rydell planned to rid the school of all the older faculty. He had nightmares that he would end up peddling vegetables in New Jersey like his father. "I'd rather die," he muttered.

"Did you say something, dear?" called Meredith.

"No. Just talking to myself. Finishing up here."

"Will you see him today?"

"Yes. I'm going now." He double checked his averages, slipped his papers into a large envelope, and took his jacket from the rack by the door. "Be back soon, Meddie," he said.

❑

Teddy was in a conference with Bob Hathaway in his office in Recitation Hall. "Now, for your last lesson, Teddy, the compound sentence, which is two simple sentences linked together by a word we call a conjunction.

Here's an example. *The boy walked to the store, and he bought a loaf of bread.* See? Two simple sentences linked by the conjunction *and,* with a comma before *and.* Write the sentence down so you can see it."

Teddy did as told, carefully putting a comma before *and.*

"Let's do another one. *Teddy is a waiter at West Hall, but he'd rather be changing a transmission on a Chevy.*"

Teddy laughed. "I've got it."

"Good," said Bob sharing the laugh.

"That's it?"

"Oh, no. There are three types of conjunctions. I made a chart for you to make it easy. I call it GREAT CONNECTORS."

"Wow!" said Teddy looking it over. "But why can't I stick with simple sentences?"

"If you only wrote simple sentences your writing would be choppy. Compound sentences smooth it out. It's like the difference between a stick shift and an automatic transmission."

Teddy looked at him slyly.

"There is more to English grammar than what I've shown you, but what we've covered should help you pass your themes."

GREAT CONNECTORS

COORDINATING CONJUNCTIONS

, AND   , OR   , FOR   , YET   , SO   , BUT

Teddy went to the store to buy milk ____ he also wanted a Snickers bar.
The car was fast ____ it was a gas guzzler.
Professor Grumitch assigned a theme ____ Teddy sharpened his pencil.

CONJUNCTIVE ADVERBS

; HOWEVER,   ; MOREOVER,   ; THEREFORE,
; THEN,   ; FURTHER,   ; CONSEQUENTLY,
; BESIDES,   ; ACCORDINGLY,   ; ALSO,   ; THUS,

Teddy went to the store for milk ____ he really wanted a Snickers bar.
The car was fast ____ it guzzled gas.

CORRELATIVE CONJUNCTIONS

EITHER / OR • NEITHER / NOR • BOTH / AND
WHETHER / OR • NOT ONLY / BUT ALSO

Teddy wanted to buy not only a carton of milk but also a Snickers bar.

The car was neither his nor hers.

❑

"I have this for Dr. Rydell," Professor Grumitch said to Marge.

She went to the Headmaster's door and peered in. "Professor Grumitch is here. Are you available?"

Rydell leaned back in his chair. "Send him in."

"Good morning, Dr. Rydell."

"Good morning, Leon. Have a seat."

Leon handed his envelope to Rydell and sat down. Rydell opened it. Grumitch had averaged all the boys' themes, which came out to C+. On another paper Rydell studied the graph Leon had drawn, which showed an upward line indicating improvement. He looked at Leon who offered a tentative smile. Rydell went over the graph again. There was something wrong, and he finally put his finger on it. "Leon, this graph assumes each boy begins with a zero, that they know nothing until they enter your class."

Leon blanched.

"Why zero?"

"Well, it's a starting point."

"Yes, but so is sixty five or one hundred. Why assume they can't even write a grocery list?"

Leon didn't know how to respond to him.

"What if a whiz-bang came to your class, someone who'd been well taught, who knew where to put the commas? Would you assign him a zero, too?"

"Well, it makes everyone start the year even, you see."

Rydell was disgusted with Leon's methodology and rationale. "Leon, I'm going to be frank with you. I want to see some of these themes your students are writing. Get them to me."

Leon was angry and fearful. "Are you building a case against me?" he blurted.

"I'm building a case for the students, Professor. Concerned you're not teaching them to write well. Is this how you've been teaching grammar for the past thirty years? I must say, I'm not impressed. Surprised this hasn't been called to your attention before. In today's world you have to be a good communicator. That's why I brought Hathaway in here, to teach the boys how to speak well. Want them to be able to write well, too. Are you up to it?"

"Well, yes. Of course, I am. I've been teaching for a long time, and I—"

"Yes, yes, I'm aware of that. Let's wrap this up. Thank you for your report. I do want to see the themes the boys are writing, particularly interested in the progress of Teddy Garcia."

"Why Garcia? Why is he singled out?"

"Because he was frustrated to the point of running away. That's drastic behavior, and, as I understand, it was triggered by your not only not getting across the lessons of grammar but also an unfounded accusation."

"I see," said Leon rising from his chair. "I'll collect the themes from the boys and have them for you Tuesday."

Leon rushed out of the Headmaster's office. He was angry. He *is* building a case to fire me, he thought. Damn that Garcia and his rashness. And Hathaway, too, that interloper, that do-gooder, that—. He spotted Teddy walking toward him from the library. "Mr. Garcia," he called.

Teddy looked up. The last person he wanted to see was Professor Grumitch. He hadn't apologized to him yet. It was something he kept postponing. He did not hurry to meet him.

Grumitch was short of breath as he approached. "I want you to come with me."

"Professor Grumitch," Teddy began, "I want to apologize for my . . . for my leaving so abruptly."

Grumitch ignored the apology. "You ran away."

"Yes," said Teddy lowering his head.

"And you blamed me."

"Well, I, ah . . ." Teddy didn't know quite how to put it.

"I have an assignment for you. It's for Dr. Rydell. He wants to see an example of your theme writing. Come to my office." Leon was pleased at the coincidence of meeting Teddy, and doubly pleased he'd have an example of a zero for Rydell today.

Teddy sat in Grumitch's office while Leon cleared a space on his desk for him to write.

"I want you to write 250 words on something. Anything. Your choice. He pushed a lined sheet of paper and a pencil to him."

"Does it have to be exactly 250 words?"

"Just write. Fill out both sides of the paper."

Teddy drummed the pencil on the paper. "I can't think of anything," he said.

Grumitch let out a frustrated sigh. "Haven't you got a scintilla of imagination? Write about, oh, write about . . . you like cars so much write about . . . that."

"My Uncle has a '50 Chevy that I like."

"Chevy. Good. Write about your Uncle's Chevy for goodness sake." Leon closed his eyes and tried to breath normally to quell his irritation.

Teddy thought and wrote carefully, laboring over each sentence to make sure it was not a fragment. He completed one side of the paper and double-checked it before turning the paper over. He checked for all the things Hathaway taught him. He was having fun, actually. He started several sentences with Introducers. He threw in a series, and in one sentence wrote an Interrupter being careful to bracket it with commas. He wrote faster on the other side the paper. He was in the flow of his story. When he came to the last sentence, he decided to try something new. He would end his theme with a compound sentence. The idea delighted him. He reached into his pocket for the GREAT CONNECTORS chart Hathaway gave him.

"Just a minute. What've you got there? Let me see that," Leon demanded holding out his hand.

"It's something that—"

"Be quiet," said Grumitch as he read the chart. "Where did you get this crib sheet?"

"Mr. Hathaway made it up for me."

A shiver went through Leon. The color left his cheeks. Fear and anger rose in him. "That is all. Leave, Garcia. I'll take this," he said waving the chart in his hand. "I want Headmaster to see this." And without even looking at Teddy's theme, he raced out the door. He couldn't wait to get to Rydell to prove Hathaway was a meddler and Teddy was a zero.

Marjorie jumped when Professor Grumitch banged open the door with such force the knob made a dent in the wall. "Is he in?"

"Yes," she gasped and started to get up from her chair, but Leon bounded past her and opened Rydell's door.

"Here," he said breathing heavily. "You want an example of Garcia's writing? Here it is fragments and all. And look at this," he said waving the chart in the air. "Hathaway is a meddler. He gave him this . . . this chart thing that I caught Garcia trying to use."

Rydell said nothing, letting Grumitch vent. He saw the fear in the man's eyes and wondered if he'd been too harsh with him. But he deserved it, he thought, because his actions caused a kid to run away. He held a paper in each hand and turned around to face the window while Leon blotted his shiny forehead with his handkerchief. Rydell turned back, placed the theme and chart side by side on his desktop. "So?"

"Don't you see? Didn't you read his theme?"

"His theme is perfect."

Leon's eyes widened. "Let me see it."

"Didn't you read it?" said Dr. Rydell pushing it to him.

Leon didn't answer as he put on his glasses, leaned over and read the penciled theme. Every sentence *was* perfect. Noun and verb, no fragments. The introductory element in one sentence was appropriately punctuated. Another sentence contained an appositive, and that, too, was punctuated perfectly. He turned the paper over and, with the exception of the incomplete last sentence, perfect. He paled and sat back in his chair.

"Are you all right, Leon?" Rydell asked noting his pallor.

"Yes, I'm just a little confused. The boy, why just a few days ago, he couldn't write a simple sentence, and now—" He rubbed his sweaty hands on his handkerchief. "And this chart."

"What's the matter with the chart?"

"Well, nothing. It's rather good. It doesn't *define* anything. It's a crib sheet."

"Or is it a summary, Professor, for after the student is *taught* the definitions?"

"Yes. You could call it that." Leon's mind was a swirl. He felt weak, trapped, light headed. "Will there be anything else?"

"No, Leon. Thank you for bringing me Garcia's theme. I'm pleased with his progress. And, Leon, take it easy on yourself. The bottom line here at Devon is that the boys learn. Is it a sin for another teacher to help a student? I would think you'd be glad for the boy, and maybe you might want to get to know Mr. Hathaway. It's up to you."

"Yes. You're right, of course," he said and walked out, shoulders hunched, handkerchief clutched in his hand.

He looked so pale when he passed Marge's desk she said, "Do you want me to call Meredith?" But he didn't hear her and pushed open the door. The cool autumn air made him feel better. There was a bench by the door, and he sat down on it till he felt his strength return. His thoughts were miles away. Fearful thoughts. Thoughts he'd not had since childhood. He was unaware of how long he sat there.

"Are you all right, dear?"

He looked up. It was Meredith. "What are you doing here?"

"Marge told me you weren't feeling well, so I drove over. Come, let's go home." She took his hand and led him to their car.

ARNIE WARREN

Saturday

Ms. Trion was upstairs looking in her closet for something to wear, the same exercise she went through last night with no decision. She seldom wore anything other than her uniform, so there was no need to buy dresses; consequently, the dresses in her closet were, in her words, "dated." I can't wear these old things, she thought, her hand brushing aside each dress with increasing speed and frustration. And I don't want to be in my uniform. Do I have time to shop for a dress? She looked at her Swiss army watch—four hours till his arrival. Without another thought, she dashed to the kitchen, grabbed her car keys, and left. I should have tended to a dress yesterday, and I don't even know if I'll find something he'll like. She gasped at the words 'that he'll like'. What am I doing? Why am I thinking like this? Why am I feeling like this? Sandy Trion you're nearly 60 years old! But the tingle she felt, the lightness in her chest—like a flitting butterfly—was real.

❏

Bob Hathaway was in the lobby ready to leave for Devon.

Gladys spotted him. "Going somewhere special, Bob?" she said with mock innocence.

"It isn't often a man gets an invitation to tea," he said absently brushing his shoulders.

"Allow me," she said exaggerating her brush strokes.

He arrived early at Devon and went to Cyrano's to pass the time.

❏

Teddy was all alone in the chapel mopping the floor; it was the bonus work his supervisor, Mr. Black, granted him. Dr. Rydell quietly entered a side door and sat in the back of the chapel.

Teddy did not see or hear him come in. He was thinking about the odd mood Professor Grumitch was in, that he'd collared him to write a theme outside of class, that he didn't seem his cheery self, and he wondered if it had anything to do with Mr. Hathaway. He was half way down the chapel aisle, rinsing his mop in the pail, when he realized he wasn't alone. He looked around and, quite surprised, saw Dr. Rydell.

"Hello, Teddy," he said.

"Hi, sir."

"When you're finished, I'd like to talk with you."

"I still have to mop the balcony."

"That's all right. Do your job, son."

If Teddy was confused before, it was nothing to what he felt now. He worked diligently, nodded to Dr. Rydell as he came to his aisle. Rydell lifted his feet so Teddy could mop under them. Rydell said nothing. After mopping the balcony floor and putting the equipment in the basement, he finally came down the aisle to Dr. Rydell.

"Have a seat, Teddy," he said. "You're gifted in automotive mechanics. That right?"

Teddy shrugged. He wasn't sure of Dr. Rydell's purpose in speaking with him, but it must be important or he wouldn't have come to the chapel and waited so long.

"Well, son, isn't that right?"

"If you mean do I love to work on cars, then yes."

"I want your honest answer to what I'm about to ask. If your mother agreed to it, would you leave Devon?"

Teddy searched Dr. Rydell's face for a sign to understand why he asked such a question, but the Headmaster was stoic. "I'd go," he said wiping his palms on his chinos.

"Where?"

"Back to Miami and work with my Uncle."

"I've got something that might change your mind." Rydell handed him a large manila envelope. "Go ahead, open it."

Teddy opened it and pulled out a brochure from the Toyota Corporation. The colorful brochure laid out a program for a boy to become a full-fledged mechanic with Toyota. It offered: co-op on the job training at a Toyota dealership, financial aid, in depth understanding of the mechanics of their cars, plus a complete set of tools. Teddy lowered the brochure and looked at Rydell. "Is this going to be a new program at Devon?"

"No, it's not. But does that interest you, Teddy?"

"Yes. Very much. But I don't understand."

"Teddy, Devon prepares boys for college, but not every one is cut out for that. I'm not saying you aren't good enough for college because I happen to think you're a bright young man with plenty of potential, but maybe you'd be happier at a vocational school that specializes in what you love to do. There are several in your home town of Miami that offer the Toyota program."

"You mean, I can transfer there? Now?"

"Read what it takes to qualify for the program."

Teddy read. "It says I have to be good in reading, math and language. Oh, oh. It says you have to have a high school diploma." He slumped in the pew.

"Teddy remember when we talked about making a commitment and finding your cause?"

"Yes."

"You already know your cause, now make a commitment to it." Rydell watched the boy touch the cover of the brochure. "Teddy, approach your homework assignments like a mechanic. Focus on the purpose of each lesson. Write down the important elements. Then cut 'em up and spread them out like the parts of an engine you're repairing. It's the same process, don't you see?"

Teddy smiled at the analogy. Dr. Rydell was helping him turn his dream into reality. He made his commitment right then. He would study hard. "Dr. Rydell. If I do well in my studies, can my Unclassified status be lifted?"

Dr. Rydell thought about his question. He hated classifying

the students, it was so obtuse. "We'll see when your grades are reviewed at the end of the year," he said standing.

❑

David was down at the soccer field playing one-on-ones with Coach Frampton when he suddenly realized what time it was. "I've gotta go, Coach. See ya." He ran off the field, up through the apple orchard and up the hill to Whittaker's Home. "Ms. Trion?" he yelled running up the stairs to his room.

"I'm getting ready," she called from her bedroom.

"I'm going to take a shower," he shouted. "Sorry to be late."

"Make it fast, young man. I want you here when he arrives." She stopped pulling down her slip to listen. "Did you hear me?"

"I'll be ready."

Sandy listened for the shower in David's room. He'd better not be late. He's got to answer the door for me.

❑

Rydell looked out his window and saw Bob Hathaway on the road below. He opened his window, "Bob, got a minute?"

Bob turned and walked up the drive to his office. Rydell met him at the door. "Want to talk with you."

"Sure," said Bob.

"Won't keep you. Come in." He sat at his desk and pushed over a copy of the Toyota brochure he gave Teddy. "Take a look at this, see if it doesn't have Garcia's name written all over it."

Bob thumbed through the brochure. "Have you shown this to Teddy?"

"Yes. He loved it," he smiled tapping his fingers together. "The prerequisite for entering Toyota's program is to have a high school diploma. I mentioned to him what you told the students in your talk in chapel."

"And?"

"Garcia is committed. Found his cause, Hathaway. I think the boy has had a change of attitude and purpose." He watched Bob's pleased expression. "That's all. Just wanted to give you a heads up." As he walked Bob to the door he said, "Professor Grumitch was in here miffed you're tutoring Teddy."

"Anything wrong with that?"

"Not by me. He showed me this conjunction chart you made."

Bob was taken aback that the chart had landed in Rydell's office. "How did he get a hold of that?"

"Long story. Bottom line. Grumitch had him write a theme this morning, and it was grammatically perfect. I saw it." He paused. "Sometimes teachers need a little shaking up. Heck, we all do." At the door he said, "He's threatened by you."

Bob thought how institutional politics always seemed to show up. He'd seen it in corporations all too frequently; leaders blocking change for fear their inadequacies will be made public, underlings afraid to express an idea for fear the boss will feel threatened and fire them. Even at a school in the boondocks of New Hampshire, an English teacher is threatened because someone tutored one of his students.

"I'll try to get to know him better. Find out what his fear is."

"Oh, I'll tell you what his fear is. He fears losing his job. He's 65, you know, retirement age. Don't think he's allowed himself to prepare for that day. He's a great Lit teacher, but . . ."

"Is he really that insecure?"

"It's in his eyes, Bob."

Bob left wondering why Rydell hadn't allayed Grumitch's fear. Was he really paving the way to fire him?

❏

Sandy examined her make-up in the mirror for the umpteenth time: underplayed, a little cover, light on the lipstick. She sprayed some Obsession in the air and dashed through the mist. She looked at her two new dresses on the bed. One was cocoa the other navy blue. She chose the cocoa. As she took the strand of pearls from her jewel box, she heard David's shower stop and not two minutes later heard the doorbell ring. Oh, that boy, that, that, "David?" This is exactly what I didn't want to have happen.

"I'll get it, Ms. Trion," David called clumping down the stairs, shirt tail flying.

She looked up at the ceiling and closed her eyes, took three deep breaths, a final check in the mirror patting non-existent wrinkles from her dress and winked at herself enjoying the joy of anticipation. "The heart never grows old," she said to the mirror. She heard their voices and tried very hard to slow her pace along the hall and down the stairs to greet Mr. Hathaway.

❑

"You just sit there, say nothing, while my world is collapsing," said Leon Grumitch to his wife.

"You brought it on yourself."

"Brought it on myself? How can you say that? I've been teaching at this school for thirty years, and this new headmaster comes in and upsets the apple cart. He's making a case against me, and he's using that Garcia boy to prove his point. Imagine, my having to defend my grading system." He gripped each arm of his club chair with his pudgy fingers. "And that Hathaway. I smelled something about him ever since I heard his David and Goliath speech, and Rydell just ate it up." He looked over at Meredith. "Can't you say something?"

"What do you want me to say? That you were perfectly correct in accusing Garcia of plagiarism? That you were perfectly correct in being upset over Hathaway teaching the boy something?" She pulled the lever on the lazy boy and stood in one motion. "Leon. For thirty years you've been walking around this campus, and this house, too, like what my mother called you, a prancing pony."

"Now, that's enough. Why are you siding with Rydell?" he said giving the chair's arm a firm slap.

"I love you, Leon, but your attitude and behavior is unnatural, most unlike you. You're fighting Rydell, and Hathaway, too."

"I am not."

"Yes, you are. You've allowed them to consume you."

He never thought she'd not support him. He was drowning in his own insecurity. He felt like he did as a teenager, paranoid that everyone was saying behind his back, "There goes the peddler's son." For 30 years he'd cultivated the persona of a highly respected academic in a fine New England prep school; about as far as you could come from a tenement flat in Elizabeth, New Jersey. He felt inadequate. He was depressed.

"You've developed a mean streak." She raised her hand as he started to speak. "You can't bear the thought that Hathaway is helping Teddy Garcia. The boy you caused to run away. You're angry at him, angry at Hathaway, whom you don't even know, and you're angry with Headmaster, and you're probably angry with me for talking like this."

"That's not true," He blurted rising from his chair. "I talked with Doc Dowd. He's feeling the same as me."

"About?"

"Forced retirement."

"Oh, Leon. Please."

"I'm serious. You think this is all the result of an overactive imagination? I assure you it's real. Rydell wants to rid the school of the senior faculty."

"What was Doc's reaction?"

"He told me Rydell asked what *his* retirement plans were."

"And on the strength of that?"

"On the strength of that, I'm right," he said sitting down again.

"Who else have you asked?"

Leon looked perplexed. "Why don't you take your husband's word for it? This isn't something you ask all over school about. My God, woman. Think."

Meredith was not amused. "You don't have to shout, Leon. I can hear you. So, what do we do?"

"I don't know."

"What did Doc say he'd do?"

"He didn't." He bent over resting his elbows on his knees and stared at the floor.

Meredith went into the kitchen and stood at the sink looking out into the back yard, then turned to Leon in the living room. "Do you think this would have come up if Garcia hadn't run away?"

"Haven't a clue, and I don't want to hear about Garcia," he said, his voice rising.

"Leon, you're in denial. Your imagination has sent you off the deep end, and now you've managed to get me upset wondering how we'll manage after Devon. You're infecting everyone around you with your negativity. Poor Doc Dowd. No telling what you've got him thinking."

Leon started to rise.

"Sit down. I'm not through," she said coming back to the living room.

"Yes, you are," he bellowed. "I've listened long enough."

"No, you haven't."

They stood face-to-face and glared at each other. Leon's breathing was labored. He turned and walked to the door, his hand trembled as he reached for the knob.

"Come back here," she demanded. "We're not finished."

"Let me know when my Meddie gets back," he said and slammed the door. He stumbled going down the three steps; his hand darted out for the railing to steady himself. He walked with difficulty across the front yard. "My God, what's happening to me?" He felt dizzy, faint, light-headed. He could feel a tingling coming from the base of his skull and spreading across the top of his head. He lost focus and fell to his knees, his hands supporting him. He was perspiring. His wrists gave out, and he fell face first on the front lawn.

Inside, Meredith was crying in the bathroom. They rarely had arguments—certainly never as harsh as this one. It made her sick to her stomach. The thought that he might be right about Rydell forcing his retirement rocked her security. She felt some horrible change was about to happen in their lives.

Teddy, walking down the hill from Cyrano's, saw Grumitch on all fours on his front lawn. He thought old Leon was picking weeds. Teddy looked off to the football field and saw two boys playing catch. When he looked back, Leon was face down on the lawn. He ran over to him. "Professor Grumitch? Are you all right?" He put his hand on Leon's back and shook him. Leon moaned. It frightened Teddy. "Come on, sir, let me help you roll over." He pulled on Leon's shoulder. Leon rolled with Teddy's pull and opened his eyes. He realized the professor couldn't focus. Teddy jumped up, ran to the house and banged on the door. "Mrs. Grumitch, Mrs. Grumitch, come quick. Something's happened to the Professor."

Meredith, sitting on the bathroom floor, raised her head.

"Mrs. Grumitch are you home?" He kept banging on the door, his heart pounding as he looked back at the motionless Professor.

Meredith reached for the sink to help her stand. Sharp pains in her eyes from the constricted blood vessels behind them. More banging. "I'm coming. I'm coming."

Teddy's jaw dropped when he saw her. She held onto the door jam for support, then she saw Leon lying on the ground.

"Oh, dear. Oh, my dear." Teddy helped her down the steps. She crumpled at her husband's side. "Oh, Leon, what have I done?" she moaned as she rocked with his hand in hers, tears streaming down her cheeks. His hand twitched. "Teddy, go inside and call Sandy Trion. Hurry, Teddy."

❑

Ms. Trion had poured the tea and now passed out the scones. She was curious to see if Bob opted for some strawberry jam to sweeten the taste. He did.

"Scones are great aren't they?" said David.

"Mmmm," said Bob taking a bite. "Delicious."

Sandy beamed at him. "So, you've been helping David."

Bob nodded.

"Mission accomplished," said David. "We've ferreted out what I'm good at."

"And?" said Sandy.

Bob said, "He likes the food industry."

"I'm not surprised," said Sandy. "He gave me some tips on making the scones."

They both looked at David.

"Something you want to say, David?" asked Bob.

"I don't know where to start. Do I go to cooking school? Do I take a job in a restaurant?"

"You told me you love to make sandwiches," said Bob.

David laughed uneasily. "Well, true, but really, how would that look in the Alumni Magazine. *David Viraldi gifted sandwich maker.* I don't think so."

Sandy said, "The Blimpie man says his sandwiches are a beautiful thing."

"Are you telling me I should apply to Blimpie's or a Subway?"

Bob leaned forward. "Ever hear of a mind-map?"

David shook his head.

"It's a visual picture of everything you could possibly think of on a specific subject. It will help you *see* your thoughts. On your flight back to Florida, you'll have plenty of time to draw one. Here's what you do. Put your key word in the center of a piece of paper. Draw lines outward, like spokes of a wheel, and write something that applies to your key word, a heading. Now, what's your key word?"

"Sandwiches?"

"Broader than that."

David looked off to his left thinking. "The food business," he said.

"Good. That's your key word. Now, think of all the things that are involved with the food business."

"You mean, like baking and broiling and stuff like that?"

"That'd be one heading. What's another?"

"Types of restaurants?"

"Yes. See how it works? Mind mapping gives you a snapshot of your thoughts that could trigger who knows what in your effort to zero in on exactly the direction to take."

Sandy put her hand on his arm. "David, when I lived in Boston, I was getting out of a cab in front of the Parker House and saw a mother and her little five year old coming up the street. The little girl was jumping and dancing, and the mother said, 'What's got into you?' And you know what the little girl said? She said, 'Mummy, my feet are so happy. They've never been to Boston before.' Here's a little girl in a strange city—no fear, no hesitation about exploring the unknown. Her message is clear, David—life's a dance, don't sit it out. Go where your heart leads you—*without fear.* Because, David, life is about doing what you love whether it's baking cookies or flying to the moon."

Bob Hathaway felt like applauding this lovely lady, this spirited woman, this woman he wanted to know more about. He smiled at her as he reached for another scone. She returned his smile and inched the strawberry jam closer to him.

The phone rang in the alcove, and Sandy excused herself.

Monday

Substitute teacher Lawrence Scott Rydell climbed the steps of Recitation Hall. He decided *he* would be the one to fill in for Professor Grumitch while Leon recuperated from his heart problem. He was qualified. He'd taught high school English after graduating from Swarthmore College. He was eager to see the boys, and his mission was to teach them grammar so they could write like champions. In typical bluster, he cared not what Grumitch had already taught them. He was going to do it his way and get results, fast.

He entered the classroom precisely at 8:00 a.m. Gregory Prindle shot up out of his chair more startled than out of respect; the others jumped up, too, clumsily uncertain where to put their hands.

"Sit," said Dr. Rydell placing his briefcase on the desk. He snapped it open and pulled out a folder. With a slight smile, he looked at each of the 12 students. He noted Teddy over on the side. Next to Teddy was the Prindle boy, father was a minister he recalled; Costantino, the football lineman, and Fogarty, who raised his hand. "Yes, Mr. Fogarty?"

"Is Professor Grumitch getting better?"

"He's doing fine. I'll tell him you boys were asking for him." He sat on the edge of the desk and folded his arms. "What do you like best about this English class?"

The boys looked at each other.

"Come, come, I'm not looking for a consensus. You, Prindle, what do you like best about this English class?"

Prindle, a shy boy, tall and bony to the extent that the boys called him Spindle, said, "The stories Professor tells us."

"Stories? What kind of stories?" He wanted a lengthy answer from Prindle to set an example for the others. They all complied recounting anecdotes of the author they were studying. (They were reading *The Old Man And The Sea* by Ernest Hemingway.) Each boy talked at length with enthusiasm to his surprise. He was impressed with their retention. Rydell had heard anecdotes from Grumitch at faculty meetings, but nothing like this. His opinion of Professor Grumitch rose as they told him how Hemingway's parents had influenced him. And the Professor had actually met Leicester Hemingway, Ernest's younger brother, who told him Ernest wasn't a genius, *"He just worked damn hard."*

"Glad you enjoy the stories about the authors," he said. "Now, let's figure out what *they* needed to know to write correctly. In a word, grammar; and twelve faces fell. "My, such enthusiasm. Did any of you make a personal commitment to learning the rules?

Did any of you make learning the grammar rules your cause as Mr. Hathaway suggested in chapel?" The boys looked away from his appraising eyes. "Let's get down to business." He took off his jacket, fitted it over the back of his chair, unbuttoned his shirt cuffs, snapped them two turns up his arm and faced the chalkboard. He wrote: Great Connectors. He placed the chalk in the tray and brushed his hands together to rid the chalk dust.

Teddy sat up at the mention of Great Connectors. He wasn't sure what Headmaster had in mind, but he was glad he had studied the chart.

"Prindle," he called, "come up and write a simple sentence." Prindle stood at the board for a moment, head down, thinking. At last, he pressed the chalk to the board and wrote: *Professor Grumitch is in the hospital.* "Fine, Prindle, have a seat. Next? Who'll write another simple sentence?" No one raised their hand. "No volunteers? Then Fogarty, you come up." Fogarty walked to the chalkboard, thought for a moment, then wrote: *We miss him.*

"Now, if we were to make one sentence out of those two, what would be your connecting word, and how would you punctuate it?" No one responded. "Very well, Garcia you come up here."

The boys snickered. Teddy Garcia would be the least likely to fulfill Rydell's request. Without hesitation he put a semicolon after the first sentence, wrote the word consequently, followed it with a comma, erased the capital "W" from the "We" in the second sentence and wrote a small "w." The class was amazed. *Professor Grumitch is in the hospital; consequently, we miss him.*

"Mr. Garcia? Is there another way to punctuate that?"

Teddy wrote. *Professor Grumitch is in the hospital, and we miss him.*

"It seems Mr. Garcia has made a commitment to studying grammar. True, Garcia?"

Teddy nodded.

Dr. Rydell passed a handout to each of the students. When Teddy received his copy, he looked up and caught Rydell's wink. Rydell had made copies of Bob Hathaway's chart. For the rest of the hour, he drilled them on the compound sentence. Each student came to the chalkboard, created a compound sentence using one of the connection words and punctuated it properly. Before they left he had them write: *"In a compound sentence, the relationship of one clause to another decides which connector to use."*

As the students filed out, he collared Teddy with a head nod. "Teddy, what else did Mr. Hathaway teach you?"

"Where to put the commas."

"Good. Make me a chart."

"A comma chart?

"Yes. Drop it by before class on Wednesday."

Teddy nodded and left.

Rydell was pleased. He had instructed and challenged them. He was so pleased that he thought he'd spend the afternoon calling alumni for donations. How could they refuse his enthusiasm?

❑

Leon Grumitch sat up in bed in a private room in the hospital. He wondered if his heart problem was his death knell at Devon. He wondered why Hathaway upset him, and he wondered if his wife still loved him in the way she had when they were young? He hoped she would visit soon. He wanted to feel her hand in his, her cheek against his.

Meredith and Sandy were talking in the visitor's lounge.

"You think he'll be all right, Sandy?"

"Cardiac arrhythmia is not that unusual, and the pace maker they inserted will prevent future black outs. He'll be fine."

Meredith swirled the coffee in her cup. "His emotional state concerns me," she confided.

"What do you mean?"

"He doesn't show it, but he's a nervous wreck wondering if Dr. Rydell is going to release him. The Garcia incident, the Hathaway tutoring . . . his imagination, or should I say paranoia, is running away with him."

"What's Bob Hathaway got to do with it, Meredith? Your husband is a brilliant man, a specialist in literature. Bob is a Speech teacher who happened to give Teddy a couple of ideas. That's all. And Teddy is just an impulsive boy."

"I just don't know what would happen to us if he were let go." She crossed her ankles and sat back in the plastic chair, both hands holding her coffee cup in her lap, shoulders slumped.

"Do you want one of these?" Sandy asked opening a packet of cheese crackers. Meredith shook her head, and Sandy opened the packet and drew out a cracker for herself. "Is there anyone Leon could talk with besides yourself that would cheer him up, allay his fears, that sort of thing?" Meredith remained still, and Sandy wondered if she had heard her question. Sandy fished another cracker from the pack. "I'm getting some more coffee. Do you want some?"

Meredith sighed, "No, thank you, Sandy. I'm fine. I was wondering," she said, her brow in a frown, "what would happen if Bob Hathaway spent some time with him?"

"To do what? I thought Leon didn't like him."

"Maybe Leon should get to know him." She stared across the room squinting in concentration. "If he got to know him, perhaps he wouldn't feel threatened."

Sandy went over to the coffee machine. The cup plunked down, the coffee poured, and the creamer made mud of it. She returned to her seat.

"Oh, Sandy, we had the worst argument just before his attack." She began to cry.

Sandy touched Meredith's arm. "Do you want to tell me about it?" She reached for the coffee cup in Meredith's hands, took it from her and watched as she dabbed her eyes with a Kleenex.

"He was trying to tell me how lost he felt, and what did I do? I told him he was way off base. I was so sharp with him." She dabbed at her eyes. "I picked the wrong time to argue the point. I didn't realize how deeply he hurt . . . how upset he was. He has nightmares . . . still . . . after all these years whenever he feels insecure. He feels if he fails he'll become like his father, a vegetable peddler. He hated his childhood. Apparently, all the mother and father did was argue. To this day, disharmony upsets him." She shook her head.

"Is that where his love of literature began? As an escape?"

"Perhaps, but I know he truly loves literature. It's not just for escape. He loves words, Sandy. He's fascinated by the mystery of creativity. So many times, he'll be reading and suddenly put the book in his lap and say, 'How on earth did the writer come up with that!'—and we'll talk about it." She gazed out the window.

"Meredith, I think you should meet with Bob and explain Leon's anxiety. He can't go on like this. It's not good for his mental or physical health."

"True."

"And you know? It's easier to talk with a stranger."

"I should see Leon now," said Meredith getting up. "Thank you, Sandy. I'll think about what you said." She disposed of her Kleenex and walked down the corridor to his room.

Sandy looked after her. She had not guessed the Professor was insecure, haunted by the dark memories. But our past is always with us, she thought. Sometimes a joy, sometimes a burden. We carry it all our lives. Best we can do is try to make sense of it, and let it go.

❑

Gladys and Bob were in the dining room when David Viraldi entered. "Well, David, to what do we owe the honor?"

"Leaving today, Mr. Hathaway."

"Want some pancakes, David?" said Gladys. "Keep your tummy from growling on your way to Boston."

"Thanks, but I've had breakfast. Mr. Hathaway, I want to thank you again for helping me get back on track."

"So, what have you decided to do?"

"Start with the mind-map like you said, then . . . look for a job."

"Will you keep me posted?"

"Yes, I will." He reached into his pocket. "Here's my address and phone number, sir."

"Thanks, David, and you can reach me here."

As they watched him leave, Gladys got comfy in her chair. "You haven't told me about the tea? I want to hear all about it."

"I told you yesterday. It went fine."

"I mean about the lady serving the tea, Bob."

"She's . . . intriguing."

"My, what an interesting word."

"Really, I look forward to seeing her again. I talked with her Sunday and complimented her on how she handled getting Leon to the hospital and all. She's a dazzling woman, Gladys."

"Dazzling. Now, that's a much better word."

Tuesday

Finally, the day had arrived for Bob's first Speech class—three weeks after the other classes had begun; Dr. Rydell wanted each student's classes set before adding to their schedules. Bob parked at the post office, said good morning to Mr. Willis and everyone else he met as he smiled his way down the hill to Recitation Hall. He opened the classroom door, and the boys scurried to their seats.

"Good morning," said Bob.

"Good morning," they mumbled.

The chairs were in a semi-circle, the boys' coats in a pile to the side. Bob put his briefcase on his desk and sat on the edge facing them. He told them that being able to stand up before a group of people to inform, excite, persuade or demonstrate something was an essential prerequisite to becoming a leader. He told them how it felt to feel the audience's silence, their concentration on your every word. He told them of the fulfillment a speaker feels when he knows his words made a difference in someone's life.

He named the famous people he'd shared the platform with, told them where his speaking skills took him: inside Fortune's foremost corporations and the management institutes of Hong Kong, Singapore, and Kuala Lumpur. He spoke of industry leaders he had privately coached. He wanted them to know he was not someone who'd majored in Speech, received degree upon degree, but never had to make a living as a professional speaker.

"This class will help you organize your thoughts, give you confidence, help you be quick on your feet and set you apart from the group. What you'll learn in this class, you'll carry with you for the rest of your life. Whenever you are asked to speak, you will accept the offer with confidence because you'll know what it takes, and your success will open many doors and lead to great opportunities. Now, take paper, take pencil."

The boys reached into their backpacks for a pad and pencil.

"First, never, *ever* memorize your speech. You can't be a good communicator standing in front of an audience focusing on your memory bank instead of them. And if something interrupts your speech, you are lost. *Never memorize your speech.*

"Secondly, *never write your speech.* Two reasons. You speak differently than you write, and, frankly, if you write your speech you might as well hand it to the audience at the door and go home.

"Thirdly, never tell a joke. You don't have the timing to tell a joke. How many times do you think it takes a comic to match his physical actions with his words to tell the joke perfectly? Twice?

Twelve times? More than once, I assure you. *Don't tell jokes.*"

One of the boys raised his hand. "Mr. Hathaway, how do you get the audience to laugh?"

"There's a difference between a joke and a funny story. A story is real and personal. A joke is not. But they have one thing in common—the punch line: two quick thoughts, seven or eight words each, and the laugh comes with the last words. Here's an example from a long ago comedienne named Totie Fields. *'I've been on a diet for two weeks. All I've lost is two weeks.'*

"Number four. *Don't open or close your speeches with a quote* from somebody. The audience came to hear you. Naturally, within your speech, you might want to quote an expert to validate what you're saying, but here's the point. If you open with a quote it comes off stilted and closing with a quote is unimaginative. Close with your own stuff."

Next, Bob had them simulate a press conference to get them on their feet. Each boy stood before the group, gave his name, where he was from, what he loved doing most, and the name of a favorite family member. The class then rapidly asked questions of the speaker just like a press conference. The purpose was to prove that when they spoke of things they knew best stage fright would not exist. "You are most comfortable when you're talking about *your* experiences. Let's start with you, Fogarty."

As each boy spoke and fielded the rapid questioning, Bob jotted down snippets of information about them.

Sean Fogarty from Marblehead, Massachusetts. Already a man: barrel chest with tufts of hair poking out of his shirt collar.

A sophomore, a shot putter on the track team, and wants to go to college in California because it's warm and "there's lots of babes." He speaks easily without hesitation. Need to help him stick to the point.

Gregory Prindle: An only child. Hobby is collecting stamps. Thinks he might become a teacher. Admits Speech class will be vital but sheer agony to go through. Kind of boy you'd find interesting to talk with, assuming you were aware of his presence. Need to raise his confidence.

Rick Hewitt is from the South. Exaggerates his drawl. Called Fogarty "Bubba" to annoy him. An honor roll student and soccer player. Boys call him "The Mouth from the South." Need to rein in his southern accent.

Perry Costantino waddles when he walks. A lineman on the football team. Legs thick as posts. No neck. Grades are average. Likes football and chocolate malts. In the summer, he hefts 100 pound sacks of grain at his father's feed store in Vermont. Called "The Coz." Need to hone his gift for humor.

Eric Windlass from New York City. Sophisticated. Keeps to himself. Cold. Dates a townie. Needs to warm up. Work with him on personal stories.

Jackie Ping from Hong Kong. Tiny boy, always smiling, looking for acceptance. Nicknamed "Pong." Giggles out of context. Won science prize in sophomore year. Cheeriest when he makes someone laugh. Excellent physical and verbal coordination. Need to rid the giggles and help him with a sense of command.

Jim Burgess from Panama. Suffers from acne. Nasal voice. Syntax excellent. Combination of acne and nasality distract from his message. Will show him voice placement to rid his nasality.

Thomas Poitier has an 'I'm better than you' arrogance, but very confident. Need to help him break through his facade.

Billy Holmes track star. Lazy tongue causing a slushy sound. Articulation drills will correct that.

Teddy Garcia. High soprano voice. Confident, a swagger in his delivery. 'I dare you' attitude needs tempering.

Bob concluded his first class by telling the boys why the 'press conference' exercise was important. "Each of you became so involved with getting your answers out spontaneously, that you spoke easily in front of the group. If you talk about things you know, there is no fear. You may feel butterflies before you speak. That's natural. But that's not nervousness. That's the result of your adrenaline pumping up your level of excitement. Don't confuse the two feelings."

As Bob left Recitation Hall, he saw Meredith Grumitch on her front lawn coming toward him.

"Hello, Mrs. Grumitch," he said. "How's your husband?"

"He's coming along, be home soon. How are you doing?"

"Fine. Just had my first class. Are you headed for Cyrano's?"

"No, just getting some air, but it is chilly isn't it?"

Bob saw a shiver go through her. "Well, give my regards to your husband."

"Mr. Hathaway," she said with some urgency, "would you have a moment to talk?"

❑

Bob was in the hospital cafeteria finishing a hamburger thinking over what Meredith had told him and wondered how he could help Leon get out of his funk. He finished up in the cafeteria and walked down the hall to Grumitch's room. He rapped lightly on the door. It swung open easily, and he saw the Professor sitting up in bed reading.

Leon looked up, puzzled at first as to who the stranger was; then the cheek, the sunken cheek . . . it was Hathaway. He lay the book in his lap and removed his glasses.

"Hello, Professor Grumitch," said Bob.

"Hello," was the curt reply. "What can I do for you?"

Bob smiled, "May I sit down?"

Leon nodded to the chair and frowned. "Who sent you?"

Bob shrugged. "Just came by to see how you're doing. I've been looking forward to meeting you."

"I'm doing fine. No pain. Ready to get back to my students," he said smoothing the sheet around him. "And how are you?"

"Everything is going well. I had my first class today."

"Speech teacher?"

"Yes," said Bob. "And Advisor. How long have you been an English teacher?"

"Thirty three years, sir," he snapped. "How long have you been teaching Speech?"

Bob smiled at how Leon had put him on the defensive. He calmly said, "Not a fraction of the time compared to you, Professor. But, I must tell you this. I've been in the communication field for over forty years. So, we've both been around the block, wouldn't you say?" He watched Leon's lips move into an imperceptible smile. "How's the food here?"

"Fine. Fine. Well, not really. It's never hot enough. Ever been in the hospit—" he caught himself and changed the subject. "Who's your favorite author? You read don't you?"

Bob smiled at the inference. "Yes, I read, Leon. May I call you Leon?"

Begrudgingly, Leon nodded.

"Last book I read was something by John Grisham."

Leon rolled his eyes. "I meant of substance."

"Well, let's not be too harsh on brother Grisham. He's an excellent communicator."

Leon had grown weary with the sparring. He didn't feel like playing pitty-pat with Hathaway, and he certainly wasn't warming to him any more than when he heard his speech in chapel. He sighed, "I guess my students are enjoying the week off."

Bob winced. Leon noticed.

"You know something I don't, Hathaway?"

"Well . . ."

"Someone is teaching my boys?" He frowned. "Not you!"

"Hardly. I believe Dr. Rydell is doing the honors."

Leon's eyes popped. "Ry*dell* is teaching my students?"

"Yes. Would you have chosen someone different?"

Leon blinked. "I . . . I never thought of that."

Bob went to the window. "Gray out isn't it?" No response from the Professor. "I wonder how authors would describe this?"

Leon jumped at the bait. "Hemingway would use a feeling adjective, Sinclair Lewis would use it to satirize a depressing character, and F. Scott Fitzgerald would wax so eloquently you'd feel the chill on the hairs of your arm."

Bob was awed by his eloquence. He could feel the pull and understood why the students loved his story telling. Bob walked to the foot of the bed. "I can see how you hold the class in the palm of your hand. I wish you were my teacher when I was a student."

"I forgot. You *are* a Devon man."

Bob turned toward the door.

"No, wait. Don't go just yet. I'd . . . I'd like to hear more about your student days back then. Pull a chair over here."

❏

"Like to see Dr. Rydell," said Teddy.

"He's in conference, Teddy, but he'll be out soon," said Marjorie. "Why don't you take a seat on the bench over there."

"Thank you," said Teddy. He listened to the rise and fall of voices behind the Headmaster's door.

The door burst open and young Lee Poole, known to his classmates as Cess, scampered out. Seems Cess had ingeniously rigged a timer in the electrical plant to knock out the electricity while the Saturday night movie was playing in the assembly hall. The ingenious part was he was in the audience when the lights went out. Someone squealed, and the Headmaster gave him a tongue-lashing and took away his off-campus privileges.

"He's available now," chirped Marjorie.

Teddy wasn't sure this was the best time to see Dr. Rydell.

"Who's out there, Marjorie," came the shout.

"Mr. Garcia to see you, sir."

"Come in, son."

Teddy smiled and handed him his comma chart.

"You've been busy I see," said Rydell scrutinizing the chart.

Teddy sat on the edge of the chair by the Headmaster's desk.

"*Interrupters* your word?"

"No, Mr. Hathaway's."

"Where'd you get this *oh, well, now, yes, no,* business?"

"Mr. Hathaway told me to memorize them. If one of those words starts a sentence, you're suppose to put a comma after it."

"I see," he said. "I like this. Good job, son."

Teddy beamed. "Thank you."

"Everything going all right?"

"Yes, sir," said Teddy standing.

"Good. That's all Teddy."

Teddy's Comma Chart

Social Letter: *Dear Mom,* *Love, Teddy*

Date: *August 23, 1900* **Address:** *Devon, New Hampshire*

Direct Address: *"When are we going to the movie, Bob?"*

Series

I like vanilla, chocolate, peach, and coffee ice cream.

When "too" means also.
Comma before and after unless "too" ends the sentence.

I, too, like ice cream. *I like ice cream, too.*

After: *Oh, Well, Now, Yes, No,*
when they begin a sentence.

No, I don't want any. Yes, I'll take some. Oh, I dropped my fork.

Now, I'll have to get a clean one. Well, that's better.

Introducers

When I was in grammar school, I played T-ball.

If you work hard enough, you can accomplish anything.

Interrupters

1. Tells more about the subject.

Mr. Hathaway, our Speech teacher, helped me with my themes.

2. An aside. Like a whisper in the reader's ear.

Mr. Hathaway, by the way, helped me with my themes.

❑

Meredith absently wiped her kitchen counter and wondered if life would be different now that Leon had heart trouble. Would his energy level change? Would his diet change? Would their lives change in some way? How would they plan for a future without Devon? They had never discussed retirement. Their lives went from season to season so predictably there seemed no urgency or immediacy to talk about it. She liked their home; right in the thick of things with students and faculty members dropping in for coffee on a break from their class at Recitation Hall. And Leon? He's stubborn and full of himself, but, oh, how he loves this place. Walking from here to his classroom and bringing back a student to talk with in the den. The students are his whole life! How can Rydell take this away from him? I fear change is on its way, and we're totally unprepared.

The phone rang.

"Hello."

"Meredith? This is Marjorie. I was just calling to see how the Professor is doing."

"He's coming along, Marjorie," she said guardedly knowing Marjorie's mission in life was not secretarial but tittle-tattler.

"I just want you to know that Dr. Rydell is happy as a clam substituting for your husband."

"Un-huh. Well, I'm sure Leon will be pleased to hear *that.*"

"And, I also wanted you to know how much he's discovered the students absolutely love your husband."

Meredith listened.

"Yes, they've told him how the Professor inspires them."

"Is there anything specific, Marjorie, that the students have said that I can share with my husband?"

"I don't know exactly what the students have told Headmaster, but I heard him on the phone this morning bragging to one of our largest donors how irreplaceable Professor Grumitch is."

Meredith heard the magic word. "Irreplaceable? He said that?"

"Yes, and . . . well, I know they had some disagreement and I . . . well, I just thought I'd pass that on to you. Hope I didn't take you from anything."

"No, not at all, Marjorie. It was kind of you to call. I'll tell the Professor. He'll be pleased."

Meredith hung up the phone, went to the foyer, put on her coat and picked up her car keys. She was going to give Leon the good news. Driving up the hill toward Cyrano's, a new thought entered her mind. Should she rely on second hand news? She turned and drove directly to the Headmaster's office.

"Come in, Meredith," said Dr. Rydell rising to greet her. "It's good to see you. Please, have a seat. How is the Professor?"

"Doing well. I understand you've taken his class?"

"Yes. I hadn't realized how much I missed teaching. Twelve bright young men headed for greatness." Rydell looked her in the eye. "Discussed with your husband my concern about how they're learning grammar. Thought I'd give it a shot," he chuckled. "And that Teddy boy? The one Leon was having a problem with? Well, he's come around. Doing just beautifully. Head of the class."

Meredith moved uncomfortably in her seat. "Wonderful," she

said, her voice strained. "And the literary side?"

"Oh, I'm leaving that to the Professor. They're reading Hemingway's, *The Old Man and the Sea*. You know what Meredith?" He leaned across his desk, hands clasped before him. "You know what I realized? I realized how extensive your husband's teachings are. The boys love him because he makes the author come alive. They told me about Hemingway fishing in Key West and Cuba. How he shot himself in the leg once fooling with a pistol on his boat, the, ah . . . Pilar, yes, the Pilar. The boys just eat it up." He paused. "What was it you wanted to see me about?"

"May I ask a hypothetical question?" Without waiting for his response she said, "What would you say if Leon retired?"

"Man can't retire," he said standing. "Can't do that. Best Lit teacher in New England. Is he thinking of retiring?"

"No, not at all. I think he'll teach forever," she said rising from her chair. "Would you come with me to see him today. I think if you shared with him what you've just told me, it would absolutely speed his recovery."

Rydell hesitated for a moment then pressed his intercom.

"Marjorie? Anything . . ."

"No, sir. You're clear to go to the hospital."

Meredith and Dr. Rydell stared at the intercom. "Woman can't help herself," he chuckled.

❑

Bob and Leon were talking about their college days and the paths they took in life.

"Are you receiving visitors?"

They turned to see Meredith peering around the door.

"Come right in, Meddie," said Leon. "I thought you were coming later."

She opened the door wide and filling the door frame was Dr. Rydell. "Leon, I hear you're doing splendidly," he smiled. "Hello, Hathaway. Well, any more visitors and we'll have to get you a suite, Professor."

Leon looked at Meredith who was beaming. "Meddie, see if the nurse can get another chair."

"We don't need another chair, I'll sit here on the bed," she said taking his hand.

Dr. Rydell stepped to the foot of the bed. "Leon, I've been substituting for your class. I think the boys will surprise you on your next theme assignment—"

Meredith squeezed Leon's hand.

"—but this is what I wanted to tell you. Professor, the boys amazed me with the information you teach them. Any teacher can recite data, but it takes a great teacher to present it the way you do. You're a master teacher, Leon. The jewel in Devon's crown."

"I . . . I don't know what to say, Headmaster," said Leon.

Rydell beamed at his own largesse. "Hathaway? Let's get some coffee in the lounge," he said putting his arm around Bob's shoulder and ushering him to the door. "Meredith, I'll take you back when you're ready. No hurry."

Leon and Meddie hugged each other. They didn't have to make a change in their lives after all. But they did. They threw away their foolish, self-created fears.

❑

Bob drove to Whittaker's Home to see Sandy.

"Just visited Professor Grumitch, and I thought you'd like an update," he smile. He recounted Meredith's concern and how Dr. Rydell layed that concern to rest.

"Isn't that wonderful? They must be terribly relieved."

She was debating whether to invite him in for a left-over scone, and he was debating whether to ask her to dinner. They both spoke at once, laughed, and Sandy said, "No, you go first."

"I wondered, I know it's short notice, but I wondered if you'd have dinner with me at Crawfords?"

"I'd love to. Yes."

As soon as Bob left, Sandy dashed upstairs and pulled the blue dress out of the closet, while he drove home thinking, *Life's a dance, don't sit it out.*

❑

In the center of the Crawford dining room ceiling was a chandelier with golden arms supporting a dozen shaded lamps. Gladys could control the ambiance by a dimmer switch. Tonight she'd set it on "romantic." The waitress led Bob and Sandy to a table.

They filled their awkward silence by studying the menu.

"What do you feel like?" he said.

"I don't know," she said running her finger along the entrées.

Bob peered over the menu. "I like your dress," he said. "Blue is my favorite color."

"Thank you," she said feeling like a schoolgirl on a date. Then she burst out laughing.

"What's so funny?"

"Us."

"Us?"

"Don't you feel like you're sixteen years old on a first date?"

Bob laughed, "Yes, I do."

"Surprise," said Gladys setting down two glasses of wine. "Tell me how you like it. It's new to the Inn." Sandy and Bob looked at each other and giggled. Gladys recommended something or other for dinner, they both said, "Yes," and she left with their menus in hand.

"Tell me, Bob, how do you teach someone to be a speaker?"

"Oh, that'd take too long. But the secret is to tell your own story and present it naturally. In other words, be you. That's not easy to do at the start."

"What do you do in class, listen and critique?"

"That's half of it. The other half is the history of today's speakers, and those roots go back to the turn of the century and the Chautauqua movement."

"And Chautauqua is . . .?"

"It began as a summer Bible school on Lake Chautauqua in New York, but expanded to include music and art and drama. They took culture to the entire country in the early 1900s. The big attraction in those days were the orators. People like William Jennings Bryan, Billy Sunday, even H. T. Whittaker."

"I'd never heard of it," said Sandy.

"Gladys told me they had a Chautauqua up here in New Hampshire, and it's still going strong in New York.

The waitress arrived with their dinners.

"Is this what we ordered?" said Bob. "Fish?"

"I really wasn't paying that much attention."

"Tell me about you? What motivated you to go into nursing?"

"I always wanted to be a nurse. Practiced bandaging on the dog when I was a kid."

They shared a blueberry cobbler for dessert and left Crawfords around ten o'clock. They'd talked for three hours, and there was so much more they wanted to know about each other. Bob wanted to ask her for another date, but he didn't want to rush things.

Back in his room, as he lay in bed, the words of Harlan T. Whittaker came to him. *'Live as though you were to die tomorrow.'* "I'll call her tomorrow," he smiled pulling the woolen blanket to his chin.

❑

Doc Dowd couldn't sleep for thinking about his friend, Leon, in the hospital. Rydell caused it, he thought, but he's not going to give *me* a heart attack. He wished Dr. Winnager, the prior headmaster, were still here. He was about tradition, excellence, and values. Rydell is about money and fancy suits. What to do about this man who controls my future? What to do? His students called Doc the 'Mighty Molecule'. He rather liked that. "Molecules are tiny but independent and held together by chemical forces. Atoms and molecules. Hmmm."

Wednesday

At breakfast, Bob had an idea: an *Evening of Chautauqua* at the Opera House. His students could speak to an audience not just their classmates. What an experience for them. And the chorus and orchestra for music, and maybe . . . maybe get Grumitch involved to complete the cultural agenda.

He went back to his room and called the Headmaster's office. Marge said he had an opening at 1:45 p.m.

❑

"Good afternoon, Mr. Hathaway," said Marjorie. "I don't suppose you have the forms for me yet."

Bob looked at her and smiled. "Surprise," he said handing her a folder. She eagerly took them and chirped, "Go right in."

"Afternoon, Bob," said Dr. Rydell waving him in from his desk. "What's up?"

"Got an idea I want to run by you."

"Shoot."

Bob laid out his plans for a Chautauqua at the Opera House. He gave Rydell the information the way Rydell liked to receive information: brief and direct.

Rydell swiveled his chair and faced the window. "I like the students presenting to all ages. Real world, Bob, I like that."

"Yes, it'll be an evening of entertainment and information for the students and the townspeople, too."

"By all means. How much is this going to cost?"

"Rental for the Opera House I guess."

"Are you going to be in charge of this?"

"Well, yes."

He spun around in his chair. "Don't think so. You'll have enough to do. I'll handle it with the Historical people. They know me there. You'll speak, too, right?"

"Yes."

"Hathaway, you've been here less than two weeks and look at the whirlwind of activity. Student runs away, Grumitch gets a heart attack, I'm back to teaching, and you want the school to produce a . . . a whatever you call it. What'll you have for me next week?" He laughed so loud Marjorie had to turn down her intercom. "This is what I want around here. New challenges, new ideas. Let's do it, Bob."

❑

On his way back to Crawfords, he stopped by the hospital to see how Grumitch was doing. His ulterior motive was to test the waters for Leon's participation in his Chautauqua idea. He tapped lightly on the half open door.

"Yes?"

Bob poked his head around, "You awake?"

"Of course, I'm awake. I'm talking to you aren't I?"

"I'm sorry, Leon, to disturb you. I'll leave."

"No, no, come in for goodness sake. Had a bad dream. Can't remember the darn thing, but it was not pleasant. You'll have to put up with a curmudgeon for a bit."

"Can I get you anything?"

Leon thought for a moment. "Yes. Yes, you can. Go out there and see if you can get me a dish of strawberry ice cream. I've a hankering for that."

"The doctor says you can have ice cream?"

"Oh, Hathaway. Who cares. Would you mind?"

"I'll see what I can do," Bob said. He went down the hall and entered an "employees only" area and barged into the kitchen.

"Patient in desperate need of strawberry ice cream. Got any?" he said to a woman in a white uniform and hair net.

"Get it yourself. In the walk-in," she pointed.

He took two scoops of the ice cream, covered the dish with plastic wrap and a towel to hide his treasure and headed back.

"What've you got in there," said a stout nurse in the hall.

"The New York Philharmonic," winked Bob.

Bob and Leon talked for an hour and covered much about Chautauqua. Bob was surprised that Leon knew of many of the performers. He told Bob about the time when Winston Churchill was booked on the circuit, but was struck by a taxi in New York City and spent most of his stay in bed.

"And I'd like you to be a part of it, too, Leon."

Leon didn't say anything but appeared thoughtful.

"Boys love your stories, and the townspeople, I know, would enjoy hearing you."

Again, no response from Leon.

"Well, think about it, please." said Bob. "You know how highly Dr. Rydell thinks of you and your talent."

The seed was planted.

Thursday

Bob was bursting to tell his students about his plan for them. He talked quickly, his excitement bubbling over. He told them how our present day speakers' lineage connects with the speakers of Chautauqua days. He wanted the boys to understand that their participation was carrying on a tradition.

He told them how Chautauqua began. "Then around 1910, Chautauqua went on the road. Their programs were seen and heard by 33 million people in 12,000 towns across America. It was the greatest cultural movement in our history.

"Picture this," he said using a voice print. (A voice print is a one or two word command to the audience that triggers their full attention. Words like —*Listen, Watch this, Picture this*—are all called voice prints.) "You're a farm boy living somewhere in Nebraska. It's 1913. There are no automobiles, no television, no radio. Transportation is by horse and wagon.

"Suddenly, the talk in town is about something with an Indian name called 'Cha-taww-kwaah.' You go to town, and you can feel the excitement. You see the window cards showing pictures of an Italian band in uniforms, lecturers posed in string ties and long black coats, magicians with top hats, singers in long gowns, quartets in matching suits.

"The rear of a horse drawn wagon going up Main Street bears a sign, 'Chautauqua is Coming.' You look up and there, strung from the dentist's office on the second floor across the street to the bookkeeper's office of the general store, is a canvas sign, 'Redpath Chautauqua.' People wear 'I'm going' buttons on their lapels.

"You run home with the news. Your folks are excited. Yes, the family is going to Chautauqua when it comes to town.

"The equipment train arrives, and you race to the field the men have mowed. There's a college boy in fancy gray pants, shirt sleeves rolled up, dropping tent pegs in a huge circle for the brown tent they'll raise.

"Next morning everything's ready, seats in place, the American flag draped above the platform and a piano to one side.

"People file in, take their seats in the hot tent, and then the musicians enter and take their seats on the platform. You're ready to burst. Finally, the mayor walks on stage and says, 'Ladies and Gentlemen, may I present, Chautauqua.'

"The band plays a fanfare. It's loud, it's brassy, sounds you've never heard before. They launch into their first piece, *The Stars and Stripes Forever.* The audience claps their hands with the beat, and when it's over everyone is on their feet applauding.

"Then the Chicago Lady Entertainers come out on stage. Four tall women with high buttoned shoes, white starched blouses, long black skirts, hair piled high and they sing and dance and talk to the audience. Their songs lift your spirits. They end with *The Battle Hymn of the Republic*. Picture that young boy, picture yourself the first time you've ever heard anything like this."

Bob brought his voice down to a near whisper. "A stage hand places a table toward the front of the stage, exits and returns with a pitcher of ice water and a glass tumbler. It is time for the main event, the speaker.

"Onto the platform comes our founder, Harlan T. Whittaker—tall, imposing, in a black suit, his long hair swept back over his ears and collar. The audience applauds, and he raises his large hands for them to cease. He nods a thank you and smiles at each section of the audience before he begins. The title of his speech is, 'Pull up your Socks, Tuck in your Shirt, and Straighten out your Attitude.' The point he makes is about the one thing no one can take away from you. Your attitude. And with a positive attitude, he says, you can go far. When he finishes—every man, woman, and child is uplifted, morally and spiritually, and each vow to do more with their lives. Young boys are encouraged to seek their fortune in the world, that they are not chained to the soil. That it's time to do great things with your life, explore all that America has to offer, and above all be true to yourself.

"Now, you're riding home under the star lit night, with only the sound of crickets and the muted clop of the horse's hoofs on the dirt road. You're on fire to go out into the world to seek the great promise of your future. That was the affect Chautauqua had on all Americans.

"Just think how you'll feel come Spring walking out on the stage of the Opera House, feeling the spot light on you, feeling the audience. You'll be carrying on the tradition of our founder and the tradition of Chautauqua. How many schools offer such an opportunity?"

The boys were all smiles. "When do we start?" asked Ping.

"Right now," said Bob. "Today, I want you to tell me about your most memorable birthday. Your talk is sixty seconds long. I want you to think about your opening line and your closing line. I'll signal you when your time is up. This exercise forces you to get to the point," he said. "Use words not emotional mosaics."

Eric Windlass raised his hand.

"Yes?"

"I don't understand what you mean by emotional mosaics?"

"Have you ever heard someone explain a movie to you like this? *'Oh, wow! You should have seen it, it was fantastic, utterly awesome, I mean the star, whoa, talk about a babe. Whew!'* And all this time the person is waving their hands all over the place. And guess what? They told you nothing about the movie verbally, but you got the impression it was a good movie because they gushed all over the place. Can you imagine a Devon History Professor saying, *'Oh, wow! Lincoln at Gettysburg. You should have heard it. Awesome. I mean, when he was finished . . . oh, man, nobody said a word. Like just fabulous. He goes, "For the people, by the people, oh, man it was unbelievable.'* Get it? A bunch of emotional impressions stuck together, passing as communication.

"All right, let's see what you can do. I'm going to give you five minutes to prepare."

"Can we use notes?" asked Sean Fogarty?

"No. And don't try to memorize it."

Bob walked to the back of the classroom and looked out the window at the athletic fields and Cottage Row and the Chapel at the top of the hill while they prepared.

"Are you ready?" Begrudging murmurs from the class. "Who'll go first?" No response. "All right, we'll start with you, Gregory."

Prindle swallowed hard, sidled out of his seat and went to the front of the room. He turned to the class and cleared his throat.

"I, ah," he cleared his throat again. "I want to tell you about my most memorable birthday. I think I was nine. Nine or ten when my parents took me to Disney World for my birthday. That's in Orlando, Florida. It's my most memorable because I got to ride Space Mountain. It's scary. I'll never forget it. And that was my favorite birthday." He rushed to his chair and sat down.

"Good start, son," said Bob. "Now, I want to caution the rest of you. Gregory spoke for only 25 seconds. I want you to speak for the full minute. All right?" They nodded and shifted in their chairs. "Sean? You're next."

Sean Fogarty stood in front of the class and grinned at his classmates. "Well, my favorite birthday was when my parents bought me a bicycle. I wanted a red Schwinn, and I got it." And for the rest of the minute, Sean described the bicycle in minute detail concluding with, "And that was my favorite birthday."

Bob nodded. He wasn't pleased with what the boys were doing. He wanted to jump in and start making suggestions, but this was their first time. Both Bob and the students were eager to get this first assignment over with. When they all had their turn, he spoke to them gently. "All right. Now, I want you to think about how you *felt* about your most memorable birthday. I want you to use some feeling talk. Not touchy-feely, I don't mean that. I mean describe your emotions. Sean, you talked at length about the bike. You described it very well, but this time I want to hear about your emotions on that special day. And who was at the party? How were they reacting to the occasion? See, we've got two things to focus on. Details about the party and how you felt about the party. Let us picture it. Let us feel it with you. Now, let's try it again."

This time Gregory Prindle talked for 45 seconds, but he only paid lip service to any emotion he felt on his birthday. He just added more details from the first speech, but Bob felt the boy made progress. "Why, Prindle, you doubled your time up here in front of the class. That's progress."

Prindle offered a weak smile.

Sean Fogarty filled out the time easily. In fact, Bob had to call him off after 90 seconds. He had no trouble at all expressing his feelings about his birthday bicycle.

Before they left, Bob gave them an example of how to make a point out of a story. A point can be made from most personal stories, and he wanted to demonstrate that for them.

"This is a story about my daughter, and the lesson she taught me. Her nickname is Doodles. When she was ten, she was on a softball team in little league back home in Miami. On Saturday afternoon, we were in the stands ready to watch her play.

"When she stepped up to the plate, her Mom snapped a photo. She wore white shorts, sneakers and knee-high socks. Across her chest was the name of the team sponsor: Ralph's Funeral Home. Her only problem was her cap. It didn't fit. Kept sliding down, covered her eyes. The catcher tried to rattle her. Doodles squinted at the pitch and whacked a line-drive single. We were astonished. First time up, she gets a single.

"Well, in the final inning the game was tied, the other team was at bat and had a runner on third base with two outs. Doodles played second base and concentrated on the batter—a big girl, big for her age. Her practice swings were so powerful you could hear the "whoosh."

"The pitcher pitched a moon ball. The batter rocked back and . . . smack . . . the ball jumped off her bat and went straight up. Everyone in the stands was gauging where the ball would fall. It would fall around second base. Doodles rushed toward the pitcher's mound. She misjudged it and back peddled—too far, too far—now she's racing forward again, looking up, visor sliding down, she stretches out her arms . . . and she catches it.

"Later, sitting around the kitchen table, I said, 'Doodles, when that ball was coming down, what were you thinking?' 'Dad, I said to myself I can either catch it or drop it. I decided to catch it.'

"She made a choice. You have choices, too. Opportunities every day to make more of yourself than you were the day before. Don't let any opportunity slip through your fingers. Like Doodles, decide to grab it."

As the students filed out of the classroom, Teddy hung back till the rest had left.

"That really happen, Mr. Hathaway?"

"It's a true story, Teddy."

"Wow. That was neat." He lingered not wanting to leave.

"How are you getting along in English?"

Teddy beamed up at him. "Great. Headmaster had me write a chart on commas. He liked it."

"I didn't know that. Good for you. Professor Grumitch will be very pleased."

"How's he doing?"

"He's coming along fine. Should be back in a week or so."

"I like Dr. Rydell's classes, but I miss hearing the Professor's stories. Well, nice talking with you. See ya."

Bob watched him skip down the stairs. You couldn't help but smile at that kid.

Winter

Winter closed in on the little town of Devon nestled in the White Mountains. Temperatures reached eight below. The Old Man of the Mountain wore a snowcap; the students wore woolen caps; and Rydell and Hathaway wore their thinking caps for the Spring Chautauqua at the Opera House.

Mr. Willis was shoveling snow from the steps of the post office as Bob pulled up and parked. Willis looked up. "Mornin', Bob." His breath sent a plume of steam in the air.

"Good morning, Mr. Willis. It's beautiful out isn't it?"

Mr. Willis nodded and continued shoveling, not inclined to chitchat. It had snowed during the night, and the morning sun made the campus sparkle. Icicles hung from the eaves of the snow covered roofs, trees with frosted limbs, and not so much as a bird's chirp in the morning stillness; only the sound of Bob's crunching steps as he walked down the hill to Leon's house. Meddie answered the door.

"Good morning," said Bob. "Is the professor up and about?"

"Come on in the kitchen. I'm making him some coffee. Would you like some?"

"Please. Decaf if you're doing instant. Good morning, Leon."

"Morning, Hathaway, have a seat."

"So, have you given any further thoughts to what you'll present at the Chautauqua?"

Leon moved in his chair as Meddie set down their coffees. "I'm not sure I want to do this. Don't know what to talk about."

"Really," said Bob surprised. "You who have so much knowledge about authors and their works. You have much to share."

"That may be true, and maybe that's the problem. There's too much to chose from. What have others talked about?"

"In Chautauqua's heyday Billy Sunday talked about moral living; fella named Colonel Bain who, get this, presented the same speech for 25 years. He called it, *If I Had Life to Live Over Again.* William Jennings Bryan talked about the *Prince of Peace* convincing people of a better life to come. Russell Conwell delivered his *Acres of Diamonds* speech over 6,000 times and people never tired of it, their ambition was stirred by it."

"Well, I'm not like one of those motivational speakers, Bob."

Bob thought for a moment. "You know what I was thinking?'

"What."

"What if . . ."

"Oh, here we go," said Leon placing his palms on the table.

"What if you por*trayed* one of your favorite authors?"

Leon looked at him as though he were crazy. "Por-*trayed*?"

"Yes."

"Like that fella who did Mark Twain?"

"Yes. Hal Holbrook, and there are a lot of people, scholarly people, Leon, who portray famous people. You could do that. Think how the town would love it."

Leon looked at Meddie. Bob didn't want to push him too hard. "Leon, take your time. Think about it. You have all the material in your head. It's waiting to be organized and presented. It'd be a shame—no selfish—if you didn't share it."

Meddie put her hand on her husband's shoulder. "I could get you a turtle neck sweater. And we could cut your hair shorter and brush it forward like Papa did and grow a beard."

"You want me to portray *Hem*ingway?"

"Give it some thought, Leon. I've got a class to teach."

❑

Rydell was in his office when the intercom buzzed.

"Dr. Rydell," called Marjorie, "it's Ms. Garcia on the phone. Teddy's mother."

Rydell picked up the phone. "Yes, Ms. Garcia, how are you?" He listened to her tell him Teddy's father had died. "I'll take care of it, Ms. Garcia. I'll call you, let you know what flight he's on and when he'll arrive. Oh, and who should he look for at the airport? Thank you. Ms. Garcia, you have our deepest sympathy." He hung up the phone and thought for a moment. "Marjorie, get me flight information from Boston to Miami for today." He turned to the computer on his desk, punched up the student's schedules to see where Teddy was.

"Dr. Rydell?"

"Yes, Marjorie."

"American Airlines leaves at 3:05 this afternoon and gets into Miami at 6:44. It's flight number—"

"Book it."

Rydell got up from his desk, pulled on his overshoes and left the building. He turned up his collar, clutched his lapels, walked down the hill and across the athletic fields to the Lab building where Teddy was taking a chemistry class with Dr. Dowd. As he entered, the bell rang, classroom doors opened, and the boys filed out nodding to the headmaster in passing. Then came Teddy.

"Hi, Dr. Rydell."

"I'm afraid I have some bad news, son." He walked the boy into an empty classroom. "Let's go in here."

They sat at two student desks. "I had a call from your mother. You father has passed away."

Teddy looked at him, mouth open. "What happened?"

"Kidney failure complicated by pneumonia." Rydell paused. "Marjorie is making plane reservations for you now, and Mr. Willis will drive you to Boston. Your uncle will meet you in Miami."

Teddy sat there, tears welling up in his eyes. "I didn't know him very well," he said.

Rydell let the boy talk.

"He was a musician in Cuba before Castro, then . . . " he

trailed off. "They beat him up in jail there. My Mom told me." He looked down, and his tears fell on the desk. "I only knew him for a couple of years. Sometimes he would talk with me, but most of the time he just sat in his chair and stared at the TV."

"I'm sure he loved you very much and was proud of you."

Teddy nodded, throat too constricted to speak.

"Want to be by yourself for a little while?"

"No, it's okay. Just kind of . . ."

"Of course. It's always that," said Dr. Rydell. He leaned forward and put his hand on Teddy's shoulder.

Teddy looked up. "Is my mother okay?"

"She seemed steady."

Teddy took a long breath, pulled out his handkerchief and blew his nose.

"Let's go back to your dorm so you can pack. I'll get Mr. Willis."

Dr. Rydell rested his arm around Teddy's shoulder as they walked to Morrow Hall. "Keep an eye out for Willis. I'll have money for you." As he walked up the hill toward the chapel, he saw Marjorie at the top waving to him. He stepped up his pace to meet her.

"He's all set," she said.

"Good. Get the keys to the Buick and meet me over at the post office, please."

Marge scurried back to the headmaster's office, and Rydell walked down Cottage Row to the post office.

"Mr. Willis?"

"I'm here," he said coming to the window. "Oh, Dr. Rydell, good morning."

"Morning, Willis. I want you to do something for me."

❏

Bob walked the short distance from the Grumitch house to Recitation Hall and his Speech class. The boys said their good mornings, and Bob started right in. "I want to show you what to do *physically* and *verbally* at the open and close of your speech.

"Physically, approach the podium and look out at the audience. Depending on the size of the audience, divide it into sections and acknowledge each with eye contact. Here in class, since we're so few, just look from one side to the other. And smile. Unless you're giving a eulogy, smile. The audience will smile right back at you, but you have to give them time to do that, and the time it takes you to look over the audience is sufficient. Let's try it."

Each boy came up to the lectern on the desk, looked from one side of the room to the other smiling all the while. Some started laughing because it felt so foolish. Bob understood and didn't scold.

"Now, then, let's practice what to do *physically* when you've finished your talk. Take two steps back, bow your head and wait. The audience will respond. Trust that. You have given them the signal that you've finished. Let's practice. Ping, you start this time."

Ping came up to the lectern, took two steps back, bowed his head, stifled his giggles and hurried to his seat.

"I know this feels awkward in the classroom, but we'll do this every time you speak so it becomes a habit. What I've shown you is what you do physically at the open and close of your speech.

"Now, let's talk about how you *verbally* open and close your speech. First, a few don'ts. Don't start like this. *'Hey, it's great to be with you folks today. Thanks for inviting me.'* Instead, hit them with a strong opening sentence. Here's a couple of examples. *Tonight, I wish I were in London.'* Or. *I spoke with the bus boy earlier this evening and asked him . . .*You see? Attention getters draw the audience in immediately. You see, people form an impression of you in the first fifteen seconds. A powerful attention getter shortens their assessment time because they're too focused on what you're going to say next.

"Now, your ending. Deliver your last sentence and *shut up.* Don't weaken it by adding, *'I hope you liked what I had to say'.* Or, *Thanks again for having me.'* End strong, step back, bow your head and wait for the applause. Got it?"

The boys nodded.

"Now, each of you explain and demonstrate what I've just said. You've two minutes to get organized."

Bob looked around the room and wondered where Teddy was.

❑

The plane took forever to fly over the Everglades. When it finally stopped at the gate, Teddy filed out to the terminal with the rest of the passengers. His uncle rushed over and hugged him.

"I'm sorry, Teddy. He's in a better place now, son."

Teddy nodded and held onto his uncle's hand as they went to

get his car in the parking garage.

The day after the funeral, Teddy and his mother sat at the kitchen table. She shared with her son stories of his father—a catharsis, the slow beginning toward the warm glow of memories that happens after a loved one dies.

"That was nice of Dr. Rydell to take care of things for you. Do you like him?"

"Yes. He's kinda looking after me."

"What do you mean?"

"Well . . ." he hesitated. He didn't want to tell his mother how he came to know Dr. Rydell so well. He didn't know how his mother would react.

"Talk to me, Teddy," she said quietly.

"You know how I like to work on cars and stuff?"

"Yes."

"Well, I explained that to the headmaster, and he thought maybe coming back here—after graduating from Devon, of course—that the Toyota program in the vocational school would be best for me. Not college."

Lyla's eyes blazed. "Not college?"

Teddy nodded. "Yuh, that's what he said."

She burst into tears, and Teddy didn't know what to do. It pained him to see his mother crying over something he had said.

"Mom, don't cry. Please. Dr. Rydell said not everybody is cut out for college."

This made her cry all the more. This was not a good time.

"Can I get you a Coke, Mom?" He couldn't think of anything

else to say.

"I want to talk with your headmaster," she said. "I'm going back with you."

"Aw, Mom. Don't do that. It's not like I'm leaving Devon."

"Teddy, you are my life." She got up from the table. "Get me your ticket. I'm calling the airlines."

❏

There was a welcome party in the faculty corner at West Hall. It was for the newly arrived wife of the history teacher, Mr. Baker. Barbara had remained in California until a buyer could be found for their home. They were talking with Leon, who was rhapsodizing over the picture perfect winters in New Hampshire while Meredith beamed at the young couple.

Dr. Rydell spent an equal amount of time with everyone yet never too long for serious conversation. No opinions sought, none offered.

Carefully watching was Dr. Timothy Dowd. His demeanor did not invite people to come by to chat. His little hands cupped a punch glass; his napkin daintily spread on his tiny knees with two Lorna Doone cookies. He observed the history teachers, the language teachers, and the english teachers chatting away, so much in common; but no one seemed interested in the molecular structure of anything. He had no one to share his interest, and, frankly, he preferred it that way. Oops, the Headmaster.

Rydell brushed a cookie crumb from his sleeve. "So, Doctor Dowd, made plans for your summer vacation yet?"

"To tell you the truth, vacation hasn't entered my mind."

"Been to Florida?"

Doc Dowd shook his head.

"They say homes are very reasonable in central Florida, and you don't have to shovel sunshine," he chuckled. "You should check it out. You know, for the golden years."

Doc smiled wanly as Rydell moved away. He carefully folded his napkin over his cookies, tucked them into his pocket, gave a quick glance around the room and left.

Bob and Sandy were standing outside talking. "Evening Doc," said Bob.

But Doctor Dowd didn't respond and scurried down the path to Cottage Two.

"Odd little man, isn't he?" said Sandy. "Lives in Cottage Two. Been there forever. His mother used to live with him. It was just the two of them for about 20 years. After she died, we thought he'd open up more, but he still keeps to himself."

"What do you suppose he thinks about?"

"I'm sure I don't know."

"I wonder if he's depressed?"

"And doesn't know it?"

Bob nodded. The conversation itself had become depressing. "Ready to go home?" he asked.

She nodded and put her arm in his, and they walked back to Whittaker's Home. The cold air made her snuggled into him.

Bob smiled. It felt so good to have her close to him.

❑

At two in the morning, Doc Dowd awoke with a start. He sat on the edge of his bed; the same kind of bed the students slept on: link springs, thin mattress, narrow. As a single man, he had developed the habit of talking to himself out loud. He couldn't stop thinking what Dr. Rydell had said to him: Central Florida, the golden years.

"Where do old faculty members retire to? Is there a special retirement community just for us? Oh, Timothy," he sighed, "did you expect to be here till you died? But I don't want to leave yet. How can I fix it so Headmaster doesn't retire me? I could . . ." He shook his head, and lay back down and stared at the ceiling, alarmed at the vivid thought he just had.

Teddy's Return

"Boys, before you utter a word you have to . . . breathe." Bob opened his briefcase, withdrew a rose and handed it to Costantino.

"Gee, Mr. Hathaway, you shouldn't have," he said, and the boys laughed.

"You'll never forget the day your teacher had you smell a rose to learn how to deep breathe. Deep breathing is all about control. Control over how many words you can say before you run out of breath. Control over phrasing. Control over volume.

"When you savor the scent of something, you don't chest breathe you deep breathe." He took a chest breath. His shoulders rose as he did so. "Now, if I say 'Good morning' all the air is uncontrollable and rushes out. Everybody try it." And just like Bob said, after their 'Good morning,' all the air from their breath rushed out proving his point.

"Now, come up front here Costantino so the class can see you. Put that rose under your nose, close your eyes and smell it. Go ahead." Coz took a deep breath. It was a chest breath, and his shoulders rose. "No, Coz, we're looking for a deep breath. Try this. Before you take your deep breath, put your right hand on your hip so that your thumb is in front and your palm feels the small of your back. Inhale the rose again, and if you've really taken a deep breath, you'll feel the expansion in the small of your back. That means you're doing it correctly. Concentrate on the scent. Do it again. Breathe in . . . feel the small of your back expand."

Coz screwed up his face in concentration and brought the rose to his nose and drank in its light aroma.

"Good, Coz. See class? His chest didn't expand like before. His shoulders didn't rise. Son, did you feel expansion in the small area in your back?"

Coz nodded and handed back the rose.

"Let me show you how controlling your breath works for you." Bob took a deep breath, held it for a second, and began talking. He recited a long paragraph of words. Throughout, he spoke softly, loudly, whispered, and returned to normal volume. "See how I could phrase and change the volume? That's control. And control comes only when you deep breathe. It's as simple as . . . smelling a rose.

"Now, we'll have a little competition. I want you to take a deep breath, hold it, then let out a thin stream of air. When you are out of breath, sit down. Last one standing is the winner. I'm going to put a stopwatch on this, so be serious."

They stood, and at Bob's signal, they took their deep breath.

Twenty-five seconds ticked by before the first boy sat down. After 35 seconds only Costantino, Fogarty, Poitier and Prindle were standing.

"When you think you're empty don't stop. Put your hands on your waist and push out all your air."

Costantino gasped and flopped in his chair. Poitier glared at Fogarty willing him to lose, he pushed on his waist to get all the air out, but he could do no more.

Prindle, surprised to find himself one away from being the winner, closed his eyes. Fogarty looked worried. He did not want to lose to Spindle. Prindle continued to release his thin stream of air. When he heard the clump beside him, he opened his eyes and saw Fogarty heaving to get oxygen. Prindle still had more to go.

"Good boy, Prindle, keep going. Fifty five, fifty six," Bob ticked off the seconds. Seventy one, seventy two . . ."

Prindle pushed on his waist "sssh,sssh,sssssssh," and he was done.

"Eighty seconds, Prindle. Way to go," said Bob. "Where did you develop such breath control?"

"Scuba diving."

❑

Mrs. Garcia parked their rental car at the post office. She and Teddy walked along Cottage Row to the headmaster's office.

"This is where you stayed last year, Teddy, isn't it?"

"Yes. Cottage Four, Mom," he said zipping up his jacket. It was 29 degrees in Northern New Hampshire.

Mrs. Garcia wore a puffy quilted jacket. They walked along the road and up the driveway to the headmaster's office. Entering, Marge looked up. "Teddy, it's so good to have you back."

"Mrs. Rawling, this is my mom."

"I'm sorry about your loss, Mrs. Garcia. If you'll wait just a minute, I'll tell Headmaster you're here. Please, have a seat," she said motioning to the bench against the wall.

Dr. Rydell came out of his office. "Mrs. Garcia, I'm so sorry about your husband. Please, come in. Teddy, it's good to have you back." As they took their seats, Rydell said, "You've a fine boy here, Mrs. Garcia. Great potential. Yes."

Teddy smiled at him, then looked away as his Mom leaned forward and put her tiny fist on the headmaster's desk.

"Dr. Rydell, Teddy tells me you think he's not college material. Is that correct?"

Rydell nodded.

"And just how did you come to that conclusion?"

Teddy looked at Dr. Rydell who returned the eye contact. Teddy was afraid the headmaster would bring up his running away.

Dr. Rydell leaned forward, put his hands together and interlaced his fingers. "Teddy, would you mind if I talked with your mother privately?"

"No, sir," he said and went outside by Marjorie's desk.

Dr. Rydell waited till the door was closed. "Mrs. Garcia, let me share something with you. When we assessed the applicants for admission, the board did not think Teddy was ready for Devon—too young, too immature to handle the regimen here. But I saw a young boy with promise. He scored well on the battery of tests we gave him. I felt he could compete in whatever arena he was tossed into. I overrode the board, and he was accepted.

"As you know, he struggled in his first year. At the end of the year, the board again brought up his name. And again, I stood by him, convinced them to give him a second chance. He's here as an unclassified freshman. Unclassified freshman means he's on academic probation."

Mrs. Garcia listened attentively. She hadn't been aware of how precarious Teddy's position was.

"He got off to a poor start this year in English composition, but has made a dramatic turnaround. A new teacher here at Devon, Bob Hathaway, took him under his wing and taught him basic grammar. Now, he's a whiz at his theme writing."

Mrs. Garcia's dark eyes softened.

"Let me show you something," he said reaching into his top draw. "I asked him to make a chart on comma usage. This is what he did." He passed the paper to her.

She looked it over carefully. "How was the Hathaway man able to do this?"

Rydell smiled. "He equated grammar with automobiles."

"Really," she said.

"The boy is fascinated with automobiles. Fixated on them. Loves what makes them run."

"So, this is why you proposed the Toyota program?"

"Exactly, but there's a catch. In order to be accepted into that program, you have to complete high school."

"I see," she said. "But he *could* go to college. I mean he might change his mind. He's very young."

"I understand, but first things first. If Teddy still wants the automotive world when he graduates, I don't see why anyone should stop him from pursuing his passion. Do you?"

"I had my heart set on that boy going to college. It would make us so proud."

"Mrs. Garcia, the Toyota program is only the first step. Who knows where it'll take him. He could advance to the corporate level. Be an executive."

She brightened at this and rested back in her chair. There was a long, thoughtful silence.

Mrs. Garcia, I want your boy to succeed."

Lyla's dark eyes sparkled. She had expected a confrontation with the powers of the school. Instead, she was greeted with kindness and concern for her son's welfare. While she had mixed feelings that Teddy might not go to college, what Dr. Rydell said made sense. At least, she acknowledged, he'll have a solid secondary education. The fact that he was applying himself was cause for great relief and pride. "I think you've done the right thing. I was imposing my wishes for him, but . . . well, the important thing is you've given him motivation to study. Thank you, Dr. Rydell. I needed to hear this from you. My son is all I have, and being a mother . . ."

"I understand. Would you like to talk more over some tea?"

Mrs. Garcia was charmed. She accepted his offer, and Teddy walked back to his room in Morrow Hall, all smiles, oblivious to the 29 degree temperature.

❑

Over the winter months, eighty-one inches of snow fell, and Teddy loved it because he could slide from the chapel all the way down the hill to Morrow Hall standing up. He no longer felt like a pariah. His classmates admired his perseverance. His writing had improved to the point where he easily balanced simple and compound sentences lending more interest and readability to his themes. This skill transferred to his Speech class. Bob noticed a rhythm to his talks. His speeches had impact because his sentences were so well constructed. Hearing of Teddy's progress filled Dr. Rydell with pride.

Meredith Grumitch noticed Sandy seemed to be gliding through the cold winter with a warm glow about her. "Woman's in love, Leon," she said. Leon grunted.

Bob Hathaway received a letter that pleased him. It was from David Viraldi, and he shared it with Sandy.

Dear Mr. Hathaway,

I'm working in the kitchen of the hotel/restaurant Chanticleer. The rooster logo is everywhere. The name and logo would not have been my first choice. Nonetheless, business is good. How can it not be with Disney World here and lots of other attractions. Great for families, and that's primarily who stay with us. The hotel has 105 rooms, so we have about 150 plus guests on average. The hotel's restaurant seats about 175. We have a large staff (23), and I've been told that soon I'll be responsible for their meals. But, I'm getting ahead of myself.

On the plane, I did as you said. I drew a mind map. I made a copy, which I've enclosed. As you can see, I figured a restaurant would offer the most possibilities of all the items on that map. When I landed in Orlando the first thing I did, before I picked up my luggage, was buy a newspaper and look in the help wanted section. That's how I found that the Chanticleer was looking for "kitchen help." So, I took a chance, went there before I went home, and I got the job on the spot. How about that!

They started me chopping celery for salads—one step above dishwasher. But I didn't mind. Now, I'm working the Fryolater. Anything fried is my responsibility. I love coordinating the fried stuff with the rest of the order the chef prepares. (I still love putting it all together.)

I enjoy being in the kitchen in the thick of the rush of waiters yelling for their orders, the clatter, the heat, the smells, and even the chef's temper. I love it. Can hardly wait to get here each day.

The most important thing you taught me was to accept my gift. I let my heart override my ego. Great feeling.

I think of Teddy sometimes and hope he's doing okay. I felt sorry for him not liking school and all, but I did admire his level of confidence. In a way, I learned something from him, too.

Please say hello to Sandy for me.

Sincerely,

David

Things were running smoothly on the Devon campus, but all was not well with one of Devon's faculty members: Dr. Dowd. Twice in conversation in West Hall, the Headmaster turned the subject to the future; sometimes about the future of the school, sometimes about the future of the country, but inevitably about his future—the future of Dr. Dowd. Rydell seemed curious as to where Timothy would settle. "Where will you retire to, Dr. Dowd," he'd ask. And Doc would shrug, look at the floor and say, "Too early to decide, Doctor Rydell." He had shared this information with Leon Grumitch, but Leon seemed disinterested, which puzzled him. Nonetheless, Rydell's message was crystal clear to him.

Each morning, after a night of erratic sleep, he felt more depressed than the day before wondering if this would be the day the headmaster asked for his resignation. And being consumed as he was, he plotted to harm the headmaster. Circumstances had forced him to sink to an uncivilized solution.

His first thought was extreme. He dared think to build a bomb. He knew exactly what he needed: dynamite, radioactive material and a remote detonator. "Hospitals have radioactive materials in their hazardous waste bin. And surely, a construction site would have dynamite for blasting the trees and granite when they cleared an area." He knew he could do it; after all, "it's only atoms and molecules."

He sat on the edge of his bed imagining pushing the remote button, the explosion, the outcome . . . "Oh, my." He shook his head and rose from the bed and went over to the window. "I can't make a bomb. What am I thinking? Why, that could destroy the Opera House! That would . . . oh, my goodness . . . kill people." And he turned his focus away from a bomb and took a shower. He continued to mumble aloud.

"But I must do something, make something that will scare him, a statement so he'll understand the pain of others. Now, what can I make that would do that? I need to make . . ." And he smiled as he thought of what he made as a young boy.

As the new year began, he gathered the chemicals together: chlorate, sulfur, aluminum and antimony sulfide. He mixed it all with sodium silicate in a mini cement mixer he'd concocted. The rotation formed little round balls. He emptied the mixer and let the little round balls dry till they were hard before drilling a hole in the top for a fuse. He had made these as a young boy for the fourth of July. They were cherry bombs. Frighteningly loud fire-crackers. He glued one on a board and wired it to a receiver. His remote would activate the receiver, cause a reaction that would explode the firecracker. He placed it in his worn leather briefcase, more like a satchel than a modern attaché case. He pulled on his rubber overshoes, put on his black wool overcoat, and set out for the woods behind Whittaker's Home.

There was snow on the ground as he trudged into the woods on this gray day. Deep in the woods, he removed the device from his briefcase, set it in the snow, adjusted the antenna and walked a distance away. He extended his arm, pointed the remote, and pushed the button. Boom! "Now, if I put a *lot* of these on a board . . ."

He retrieved the burnt board, pushed it and the remote into his briefcase. "I'll shock him into leaving. He'll be jumping at his own shadow. Fear will make him resign."

It was three o'clock in the afternoon, and Sandy Trion was having tea on her sunless sun porch. She gazed out the window at nothing in particular, when, of all people, Doctor Dowd walked out of the woods with briefcase in hand. What's he doing in the woods with his briefcase? she thought, but dismissed the oddity knowing it was in keeping with Doc's reputation.

Chautauqua

Canadian geese honked the arrival of spring, which brought Bob Hathaway closer to Devon's *Evening of Chautauqua*. Music director, Salvatore Ronciglione, had worked with Bob on the orchestral program: marches, classics and turn of the century songs. Mr. R., as the students called him, had rehearsed them with constant harping to stay in tune and, "Attack, attack, attack. Don't come in meekly," he'd yell in frustration. "Now, again."

Leon Grumitch suffered the most angst preparing his Hemingway portrayal. "What do I do with my hands? When I'm teaching, I don't even think about them. I've always got a piece of chalk or a book in my hand." And Bob said, "Touch fingers. Put your arms at your waist, bring your hands together and touch fingers. Or, try this. Let your hands fall to your side and render them useless. Try it." Leon tried it both ways and couldn't get over how comfortable it felt.

Leon's biggest problem was how to begin his presentation. "Where do I start? I know all about the man, I've read everything he wrote, but I can't figure out how to begin. Any ideas, Hathaway?"

"Leon," said Bob, "start with something he said that sums up his life; something from his childhood that was prophetic."

Bob's speech students had exhausted all their experiences as he constantly had them telling personal stories. "Tell a story, make a point; tell a story, make a point." He made them think, really think, about their opening and closing sentences. He taught them how to make persuasive speeches, demonstration speeches, informative speeches, and even humorous speeches to get them to hone punch lines. He coached each boy citing his strengths and weaknesses, but he never once tried to change their style. He wanted to enhance what was already theirs.

He took them to the Opera House. "I want each of you to walk around this hall," he said as they'd gathered by the stage. "Go upstairs to the balcony. Sit in a seat and look at the stage. This will give you a sense of how broad your gestures will need to be. Concentrate on making this hall your living room. Then come back and walk around on the stage. Feel it. Talk out loud and listen to the sound of the hall." He even prevailed upon the lighting man to come and turn on the spotlights so they could feel what it was like with the light in their eyes and not being able to see the audience.

"And one other thing," he cautioned. "Do not drink sodas, milk, even chew breath mints two hours before you speak because they coat the vocal cords, and you'll spend your time on stage clearing your throat."

"What *should* we drink, sir?" asked Teddy.

"Warm water. Keeps the throat moist."

❏

At 3:00 a.m., the day of Chautauqua, Timothy Dowd slipped out of Cottage Two with his briefcase in one hand and a flashlight in the other. He made his way down the hill, through the woods and out onto the road to the Opera House. He had attended the dress rehearsal the preceding evening and knew exactly where Dr. Rydell would be standing on stage.

The stage door faced the river. A dumpster blocked headlights from cars coming over the bridge into town. The door was unlocked; something he had checked on several occasions.

In the darkness inside, he shielded his flashlight and aimed it at the floor. He inched his way to the small door that opened for passage beneath the stage. He stopped, listened. Silence. He opened the door carefully, knelt down on his hands and knees, pushed his briefcase forward and crawled toward center stage. He felt very alert; his senses acute. He scanned the underside of the stage with his light until he found the trap door, exactly where Dr. Rydell stood during dress rehearsal.

He pulled his briefcase to him, opened it and drew out the board with forty-five cherry bombs and the detonator glued to it. He reached in the briefcase again for duct tape and scissors. He cut lengths of tape and fixed half of each to the bottom of the board. He lay on his back, drew up his knees, squeezed the flashlight between them and fixed the board to the trap door pressing the duct tape hard against the wood. "Can't have this falling off now can we, Timmy," he whispered. He gave the board a tug and was satisfied it was secure. He was convinced his ingenuity would secure his tenure at Devon.

Just before he left the Opera House, he shone his flashlight on his wristwatch. It had taken him 50 minutes. He opened the stage door slowly, peered outside for a sign of anyone, and hurried through the woods to Cottage Two.

As he climbed the stairs to his room, a student sleepily came down the hall from the bathroom.

"Oh, hello, Doctor Dowd," he yawned and went to his room.

Dr. Dowd stood wide-eyed. My goodness. I didn't expect to see anyone, he thought. I wonder if he'll remember in the morning. He went to his room, a veneer of perspiration on his forehead.

The day finally arrived, the air filled with the tension of anticipation. Bob and Sandy arrived at the Opera House at 4:30 p.m. so Bob could walk through his speech. His purpose was to check where he wanted to be physically at certain points in his talk, and he wanted to be familiar with the prop he'd brought. He didn't want to move around from side to side too much because, as he'd taught his boys, "The more you move around, the more you lose your force." Sandy watched him from the front row until he was finished.

"What's it look like from up there," she asked.

"Come on up and see," he said indicating the curtain to the side of the stage.

Sandy joined him at center stage. "Oh, my! Don't you get

nervous in front of all the people out there?"

"Exhilarated, Sandy. Never nervous," he grinned.

She walked around to get the feeling of the size of the stage. She understood why Bob wanted to practice his movements. She came back to him and looked at the stage floor, at the trap door. "Do they still use these?" she said pointing downward.

"Depends on the show. Shakespeare used them a lot for the appearance and disappearance of ghosts and characters. Some stages have elevators below that can bring up props, big stuff you know. There's more activity *back* stage than on stage. Have you ever heard the expression, 'It's bad luck to whistle back stage.'?"

Sandy shook her head.

"In the old days, stage hands cued one another by whistling to raise and lower things through the trap door. If they whistled at the wrong time, it could cause an accident. That's how that superstition began. Hey, let's go over to Crawford's for a bite."

"Too early, but I'll have a salad or something. Just like being with you."

The student body and faculty were on their way to the Opera House, and the residents, who'd seen the boys in town but never at a school event, were filing in and choosing their seats.

Backstage, Dr. Rydell walked about rehearsing his opening remarks. Meredith Grumitch, in a dressing room, brushed her husband's hair forward while Leon, in his cable knit turtleneck sweater, admired his salt and pepper beard. The orchestra tuned up behind a scrim, the chorus, triple quartet and Bob's students milled about. Time did not permit all of Bob's students to speak, so they'd drawn names out of a hat to choose the five who would.

Bob walked down the aisle of the hall, brushed aside the curtain adjacent to the stage and went backstage.

Dr. Rydell approached him. "Big night's here."

Bob smiled. "How long are your opening remarks?"

"Short," he said walking away.

Bob called the boys together. "Listen. Before you take your places on stage, check each other out. Hair in place, tie snug and straight, jacket buttoned, that sort of thing. Any questions?" The boys nodded 'no.' "Do you have your opening sentence ready?" Again they nodded. "What are you going to do before you walk up to speak?"

"Pray," said Pringle.

Teddy offered, "Deep breath and let the air out slowly."

Bob smiled and nodded. That was the right answer to help a speaker relax and be in control. He went out to the hall through the curtained doorway, up the aisle to the rear of the House to watch at a shoulder height partition behind the last row.

Timothy Dowd had arrived early to be sure to have a seat in the back row. He put his remote on his thigh and covered it with his palm.

The audience applauded as Dr. Rydell strode on stage. He bowed his head in acknowledgement. Doc Dowd straightened in his seat looking between the heads of the couple seated in front of him.

Rydell welcomed everyone graciously, told them briefly of the Chautauqua tradition and mentioned that the founder of Devon, Harlan T. Whittaker, was one of the premier speakers on the circuit and that tonight's program recaptured what people saw back then—music, drama, and a speaker.

Why doesn't he move to center stage, Dowd thought.

Dr. Rydell had only come a third of the way out, not center stage as Doc Dowd had anticipated. Timothy, remote in hand, waited for the moment that never came. Rydell introduced the head of the music department, Salvatore Ronciglione, and exited. Timothy sat back in his seat. He felt betrayed. "But he stood at center stage last night." A comment that surprised the man seated next to him. "Perhaps later," he mumbled. Surely, with an ego as large as Rydell's he would eventually take center stage, he thought.

The scrim opened, the lights came up, and the orchestra played the fanfare of Wagner's, *March from Tannhäuser.* The maestro led them vigorously through five pieces concluding with Sousa's, *Stars and Stripes Forever.* He had said to Bob, when they discussed the program, that he would like to fire up the audience, "Get their blood boiling."

Mr. Ronciglione stepped forward as the scrim behind him closed and the boys in the triple quartet filed out from the wings. He nodded to the boy at the far left, a bell note was sounded, and in a crystal clear voice, the boy soprano sang, *Annie Laurie.* The other singers joined him for the second verse of the song. *Listen to the Mockin' Bird* was next with one boy contributing the bird whistle, which amused the audience. Then a medley of Stephen Foster songs and, for their final number, accompanied by the orchestra, they ripped through a rousing arrangement of, *Are You from Dixie, I said from Dixie.* They bowed to the applause, and Mr. Ronciglione led them off stage.

Dr. Rydell, who had taken a seat in the balcony with the other faculty members, was pleased. Sandy beamed, but Meredith was tense for Leon, still to appear on the program. Bob took a deep breath. His boys were next.

Three stagehands placed five chairs in a semicircle on the stage behind a spotlight for the speaker. The audience was quiet, just the occasional throat clearing. The boys took their places on the shadowy stage, and Teddy walked into the pool of light. Dr. Rydell drew a breath and sat up, Sandy touched her throat, and Bob stood motionless at the back of the hall.

Teddy smiled at each section of the audience, hands touching fingers. He took a deep breath, held it for a fraction of a second and began with his strong first sentence.

"I want to tell you about a man who taught me the most important word in my life without ever mentioning that word. A man who isn't with me anymore. My father.

"He grew up in Havana, Cuba. He played the trumpet. My mother said it was bright and brassy like him. She sang with his band, and they were very popular. But when Fidel Castro took over he got less work, and he complained about it from the stage. He said what he believed, and for that they arrested him. My mother escaped to Miami where I was born.

"I was 10 years old when my father was freed from prison. We could hardly wait to see him. We counted the days, the hours, the minutes; we decorated the house with streamers and welcome home signs. I expected to see my father with a big smile and a trumpet in his hand. When the car pulled up to our house a frail man got out of the car. I heard my mother gasp before she ran to him. She helped him into the house and to the couch in the living room. I stood in front of him. He said nothing, not even a smile. He didn't know who I was.

"It was an awful time in the house during those days because, well, here we had the closest member of our family with us, yet we might just as well have pulled a stranger off the street.

"My mother runs a Cuban community center, and she's seen those who come from Castro's jails and how slow the process is to rid their fears and nightmares. Sometimes, when I'd be lying in bed at night, I could hear her singing softly to him the songs she sang when they performed together. I guess she was trying to bring back good memories.

"On my eleventh birthday they all sang Happy Birthday, and I saw him mouth the words and smile at me. It was the first time we made contact if you know what I mean. I guess he finally knew I was his son."

Teddy paused, looked down, then through tight lips said, "My father died four months ago." He paused again. "Only now do I realize the word he taught me—without his ever saying it. The word is courage." Pause. "The courage to be yourself."

He took two steps back and waited for the applause that Mr. Hathaway said would come. The audience was too moved to applaud right away. Then from the balcony, Dr. Rydell clapped his hands and the audience followed, and Teddy stepped out of the spot light.

"Do you want a tissue, Dr. Rydell?" said Sandy.

He looked at her through misty eyes. "Not necessary," he said reaching for his handkerchief. Then he leaned over to her and whispered, "I'm so proud of that boy."

Sean Fogarty came forward. "When I was in the fifth grade, I was madly in love with Carolyn Booth. I took her to a movie. It was my first date. Carolyn wore an overcoat with big patch pockets on the sides. When we're in the movie, she folds it, hands it to me, and I put it on the seat beside me. Then I put my arm over the back of her chair trying to get the nerve to lower it around her shoulder. I waited so long my arm fell asleep. And then the pain started. You have no idea the pain. Right in my biceps. I can't move." Fogarty had the audience laughing. He was a natural. They loved him. "When it was time to leave, I pick up her coat—upside down—and *marbles* fall out. She'd brought her *marble* collection with her, and they're rolling down the entire theatre, bouncing and banging up against the stage, and everybody's turning around. Oh, man, so embarrassing." He gave a heavy sigh. "One date with Fogarty, and she loses her marbles."

The audience laughed and applauded. Bob was pleased with Fogarty's punch line: short with the laugh line on the last phrase.

Gregory Prindle stepped into the spotlight and turned his head at the brightness as though shying away from it. He couldn't see the audience and felt disoriented, but he forged ahead and told an interesting story of the history of one of the stamps from his collection. Bob was proud of Prindle for he not only conquered his discomfort but used the pause so effectively he made the audience feel he was thinking of the exact words to use at that moment.

Costantino told what it was like being a lineman on the football team. Specifically, what it's like to take a stance across from someone bigger and stronger during a big game. How he got bloodied on every down. "Every time I came to the sidelines coach would say, 'He's testing you, son. He's testing you.' By the fourth quarter I was dragging myself off the field. My nose was bleeding, my elbows were skinned, and I was hot and dirty and again the coach says, 'He's testing you, son. He's testing you.' I yelled at him, "Who's testing me?" Coach pointed to the sky and said, 'God.'"

Both God and Costantino were applauded.

Finally, Eric Windlass came into the spotlight, and his girl friend, the townie, squirmed in her seat and leaned into her mother. "There's Eric, Mom," which drew no response from the mother.

"When I was young, my parents sent me to pre-school. I don't remember learning anything in particular, but I do remember that the teacher had a way of getting us to do things with hand signals.

"On this particular day, she signaled us to sit on the floor. There were eighteen of us. We had our heels drawn up so we could lean on our knees and listen. She said, 'Today, I'm going to teach you a new word.' The word was responsibility, and she clapped for each of the syllables." Eric repeated the word and clapped to demonstrate.

"She told us that at the end of every day she had to pick up all the toys and put them back into the box. Today, she said, she wasn't going to do that anymore; that it was our re-spon-si-bil-i-ty to put the toys back." Eric, said the word slowly and clapped his hands. He asked the audience to participate. They clapped their hands on each syllable and said, RE-SPON-SI-BIL-I-TY. "And every afternoon, as our parents came to pick us up, she would simply clap her hands like that, and we'd race around the room picking up our toys and putting them back in the box.

"Today, when I have a responsibility to do something, I have to do it right then and there. It's the only way to stop the clapping in my head."

It was time for a fifteen-minute intermission. Bob went outside. Sandy found him pacing on the sidewalk.

"Isn't it wonderful?" she said. "Aren't you pleased with the boys?"

"Very," he said. "What's Rydell's reaction?"

"Don't tell him I said so, but Teddy's speech made him cry."

Bob smiled. "Teddy really came through didn't he? All of them did, and the orchestra was in tune. Mr. Ronciglione has done a marvelous job with them."

"How are you?"

"I'm fine. Eager to get on with it."

"I've never spoken before an audience, so I don't know how you feel. I know I'd be scared to death, but you . . . you've had so much experience, this must be a cake walk for you."

"It's never a cake walk, Sandy. The butterflies show up every time."

"Nervous?"

"Excited." He looked at his watch. "We'd better get back."

When every one was seated, the lighting man aimed a pin spot on the corner of the stage, Dr. Rydell walked to the spot to introduce Professor Grumitch. Doc Dowd came to attention, but knew from the dress rehearsal that Rydell would stay in that position. But he was ready in case things changed.

Dr. Rydell told the audience of the Professor's background, his dedication to the teaching profession and to Devon. He explained that the Professor taught English Literature, that his depth of knowledge of the authors and their lives was extraordinary, and tonight he was portraying one of America's great authors . . . Ernest Hemingway.

Rydell exited, and, after a pause, Leon stepped into the pin spot and stood letting the audience see the likeness he had created. While Leon was two inches shorter than the real Hemingway, his build and weight (210 pounds) fit the image. Bob watched from the rear of the hall.

"Fraid of nothing," he shouted. "Fraid of nothing. That's what my mother claims I said when I was three years old. I don't know why I said that or where I heard that, but that's how I've lived my life. It's the ideal behavior in the face of adversity. An ideal I was born with."

In a flash, the entire stage was lit revealing a wing chair to the right with table and lamp; in center stage, a couch with a sofa table behind it; and on the left side of the stage a stand up desk with paper, an old typewriter, a box of pencils and a stack of books.

Leon walked to the desk. "I write standing up, you see. Too painful for me to sit at the typewriter anymore." He picked up a book. "This was the first big one, *Farewell to Arms*. I drove an ambulance in Italy in World War I. Caught an explosive in the leg and still have the scars. Two hundred and twenty seven of them. I fell madly in love with the nurse who took care of me. I told her I loved her, but she told me she was already in love with a Neapolitan. When I heard that, I went back to bed with a temperature. God, I loved that woman. Agnes was her name. Agnes Hannah Von Kurowsky. After she rejected me, I wrote a friend of hers and said if Agnes ever comes to New York, I hope she falls down on the gangplank and knocks her teeth out. Juvenile of me wasn't it? But her loving kindness to me in the hospital was the model for Catherine in this book."

Leon put the book down and crossed to the wing chair. "A lot of people, young writers in particular, ask me how I became a writer. I grew up in Oak Park, Illinois. My mother was a music teacher, and she introduced me to the arts. She took me to nearby Chicago to the theater and museums. She helped develop my creative talent. My father was a physician who loved to hunt and fish. From him I learned the love of nature. I wrote the Nick Adams stories from the experiences of hunting and fishing and camping with my father.

"Back in 1917, I visited the Kansas City Star. I remember walking into a big room filled with typewriters and reporters, copy editors, sportswriters, columnists and critics, row after row of them, and I knew that's where I wanted to be. I got a job at the Star, and they taught me accuracy, immediacy and economy. But I yearned to go to Paris where the big names were. Gertrude Stein, Fitzgerald, John Dos Passos, Ezra Pound and such. I went there with a goal to write a perfect sentence." Leon paused. "I wrote six."

The audience was held by Leon's easy manner. He coupled Hemingway's life experiences with how they became the subjects of his books. He read to them the last section of *The Sun Also Rises.* When he finished he said, "That last sentence . . . I wrote and re-wrote it 80 times. I mentioned that to someone, and they said 'Why?' I told them, 'To get the words right.'"

He ended dramatically, letting loose a stream of consciousness bemoaning his aches and pains, his loss of ambition, his desire not to live anymore. The Professor walked off stage, and on cue, a gunshot was heard and the stage went black. It was chilling.

The orchestra began a high school arrangement of *Valse Triste*; a perfect transition filled with minor and major chords—reflecting what the audience was feeling. After a suitable pause, the scrim opened and Mr. R. led the orchestra in the *Washington Post March.* Several more selections and a final appearance of the triple quartet with the Devon chorus (40 boys) on stage singing a dreamy, melancholy turn of the century song, *On the Banks of the Wabash.* With the applause still in full force, Mr. R. cued the drummer who slow rolled a funereal cadence. *Brrrum. Brrrum. Brrrum, brum, brum.* The trumpets attacked a chord and held it for four beats as the drummer continued, and the boys sang, *The Battle Hymn of the Republic.* At the rousing conclusion, the audience stood and applauded; some wiped away tears.

The stage was quickly reset: wing chair and table for a pitcher of water and a glass and a waist high pedestal at center stage. Five beat pause, and Bob Hathaway walked out to a collective "awww" from the audience when they saw he was pulling a little red wagon. He picked it up, placed it on the pedestal, and set it so the audience could see it was a genuine Radio Flyer.

"There isn't a soul here tonight who hasn't seen a little red wagon. It is with us all our lives. How you relate to it as an adult determines how you will live your life." He scanned the audience from right to left as he repeated the sentence, bringing his hand forward and tapping the air as though the statement was invisibly passing by. *"How you relate to your little red wagon determines how you will live your life.*

"Some get behind their red wagon and push it. Look what happens?" Bob pushed on the wagon, and it zigged and zagged. "See? No focus."

He came forward. "I once gave a talk to a realty company. The preceding night the owner, Mr. Watson, showed me a huge notebook. Each page listed a property. 'My goal,' he said, 'was to own 100 by the time I was 50.' There were 125.

"My son was in a college nearby. I thought a talk with Mr. Watson would be good for him, and Watson agreed to a meeting. The next week my son called. 'Dad, I heard from Mr. Watson. He asked me what I wanted. I told him I wanted to be an entrepreneur. He said, 'You want to know the secret to success? I'll tell you the secret. Focus, focus, focus, focus, focus, focus.' 'Then he hung up on me. Bang! Just like that.' "

Bob returned to the red wagon. "When you push from behind, your head is down, you can't see the road ahead of you. You have no focus.

"Then there are those who prefer to ride in the wagon. 'Take me here, take me there.' Listen. When you ride in someone else's wagon you're going where *they* want to go. You're just along for the ride. Is that going to be your epitaph? Here lies, John, he was just along for the ride.

"Some won't even touch the little red wagon. 'Too risky, might tip over, might scrape my knees, might have to go to the hospital, this might happen, that might happen.' Folks who are unwilling to take risks in life aren't living. The Wall Street Journal surveyed retirees and asked what they would have done differently in their lives. They all said, 'I would have taken more risks.'

"What happens when you take a risk? The down side is you might fail, but that's how you gain experience and experience is how you gain wisdom. You learn more from failure than you do success. When you were a child your Dad sat on the living room floor ten feet away from you. Your Mom had you standing holding your arms up and said, 'Walk to Daddy.' And what did you do? You took one step and boom, you fell down. You failed at walking on your first try. Get the message? Failure is your first step toward success.

"All right," he said pointing to the red wagon on the pedestal. "We've seen that pushing gets you nowhere. Sitting in it fulfills someone else's goal, and not getting involved with it indicates fear—fear of success or fear of failure.

"But those of independent spirit, they take the handle and lead their red wagon—a wagon carrying their knowledge, their experiences, their failures and their successes.

"Most of you don't know what you want to do when you grow up. And since it takes twelve to fifteen years to master what you've chosen to do, you don't really have to decide on a career until you're in your thirties. In fact, you'll probably enjoy several careers, not jobs, *careers* in your lifetime because that's the world today. You may falter along the way, but the important thing is to take the handle of your little red wagon and go forward.

"Going forward, you begin a pattern that repeats itself over and over in everything you attempt to do. The pattern never changes. It's the same pattern you find in great literature, the same pattern in great movies, it's the pattern of all the great inventors, the pattern of the pioneers of America who dared follow their dreams, dared to take their wagon where their heart led them. There's a name for this pattern. It is called the hero's journey."

"Go back to King Arthur's time. A man decides to become a knight. He has obstacles. Some are so great he needs counsel, and Merlin, the wise man, appears. Now comes his biggest challenge—the supreme ordeal—slay the fire-breathing dragon and rescue the damsel in the tower. He slays the dragon and rescues the lady. He is changed forever. The pattern is complete, he's ready to face his next challenge, and the pattern will repeat itself.

"It's the same pattern you've experienced in the classes you take in school. You enter class, your first step. There are obstacles, but you keep on. Then you flunk a test and have to seek the counsel of a wise man or woman. It could be your teacher or your advisor. Then comes the final exam. That's your supreme ordeal. Do you quit? Of course, not. You take the test. You pass and are changed forever because you have more knowledge."

Dr. Rydell leaned forward. This was exactly the sort of thing he wanted all Devon boys to hear.

"Whatever you undertake in life, if you know the pattern of events that will occur, you'll know where you are at any given moment in your quest.

"Let's make up a story to show you the pattern. How about a story of a young man who loves to make sandwiches and wants to have his own sandwich business?"

Sandy said, "Oh, my gosh."

Dr. Rydell leaned over. "What?"

"Nothing," she said.

"What should we name him?" he asks the audience.

"Sam," shouted one boy. "Sam the sandwich man," said another. The audience laughed.

"Sam it is then, and he's just like you when you get excited about something. Let's take him on his hero's journey.

"Sam tells his friends what he's going to do, and he's surprised that not everyone shares his excitement. Some support him, but many say, 'Are you crazy?' 'Why would you take such a risk?' 'Hey, get a job with a regular pay check.'

"Sam is confused. So much negativity has made him unsure. Will Sam follow the advice of friends who focus on pessimistic views of the future? Friends who discourage him from taking risks? Who plant the seeds of doubt in his mind? Or should he be true to his heart and lead his little red wagon? What should Sam do?" he asks the audience.

"Go for it," they shout.

"That's the second step in the pattern—overriding naysayers and recommitting to your cause.

"Sam goes to the bank for a loan to open his sandwich shop. They turn him down because he has no track record. Discouraged, he goes to the public park, sits on a bench and reconsiders. An old woman, feeding pigeons, is sitting across the path from him. She looks over and says, 'What brings you to the park today?' Sam didn't want to get involved but politely answers, 'Oh, just to get away for a bit.' She smiles and continues to strew birdseed to the pigeons. 'If you're trying to sort out a problem, I'd be glad to listen,' she said.

"Sam reluctantly tells her what he wants to do. The old woman listens carefully. Sam asks, 'Do you think I'm being a dreamer?'

She brushes bird seed from her hands and faces Sam directly. 'Dreams are unchallenged reality. Dreams are what get you somewhere, but to make them come true you must act and have faith you will succeed. Get a bicycle and put a box on the rear fender for your sandwiches. Then, ride down to the courthouse and catch people coming out at lunch time.'

"Who was this old woman? She's Merlin in the hero's journey. She's the advisor. She's part of the pattern. And let me say to you right now that there's a Merlin out there waiting to counsel each one of you. Look for the Advisor, the Counselor, your Merlin." He steadied his gaze at each section of the audience.

"Sam buys a bicycle, puts twenty sandwiches into the box and rides to the courthouse. To his surprise there are two hot dog stands already there. Sam waits for the people to come out and when they do, he sells all of his sandwiches. He's thrilled, filled with confidence and eager for the next day, but when he arrives, a policeman hands him a citation for not having a business license.

"It wasn't enough that friends told him not to do this, now the law is putting obstacles in his way." Bob asked the audience. "Should he quit?"

"No," shouted the students.

"All right. He gets the license. Two years pass and Sam now has a truck whose side drops down to display his sandwiches. He drives all over town. Construction sites are a big money maker. He has two employees. He makes sandwiches and desserts. And salads, he discovers, are big sellers.

"Three more years pass. It hasn't all been rosy. He's tested time and time again—trouble with the truck, an employee quits, gas prices rise eating into his profits, but he has faced each obstacle and prevailed.

"Now, he feels he can make his dream come true. The dream of having his own catering business. He leases a store, stocks it with gourmet items like imported cheese and wine. He prepares hot take-out lunches with offerings as common as tuna salad to exotic Indian foods with tangy sauces. People discover his store. Things couldn't be better, but the supreme ordeal is yet to come.

"One night he gets a call. There's been a fire. Sam's store has burned down. Ruined. The supreme ordeal is here. No different from the knight's supreme ordeal when he faced the fire-breathing dragon. No different from you facing your final exam.

"Sam feels lost. Do you feel that way at times? Lost? The world against you? Look," he said pointing to the little red wagon. "What's your position? Sam only sees the handle. He grabs it and walks through the ashes of despair knowing this is part of the pattern, a defining moment in his life. Sam will go forward. He's tempered by the testing. He knows it's part of the hero's life."

Bob walked to the apron of the stage, close to the audience. *"Don't you see? You are the red wagon. Its significance and power is within each of you. Make a commitment, now, to take charge of your life, lead your wagon with daring, courage, and eager anticipation of the events in your life that you . . .YOU will initiate. The hero's life is adventurous, filled with challenges, accomplishments, learning, fulfillment, and satisfaction. Promise yourself you won't sit in it and let someone else lead your life for you. Promise yourself you won't push the wagon with no focus. Promise yourself you will wake up every morning eager to fulfill the gift your Creator has given you as you go where the heroes before you have gone."*

Bob took the little red wagon down from the pedestal and set it on the floor. He stared at it, drawing the audience to it. He walked around it as though weighing his options, and then he took the handle firmly in his hand and left the stage.

Over the wave of applause, Dr. Rydell said to Sandy, "We must have Bob deliver this message to the incoming freshman." And he quickly made his way to the stage.

The audience stood and clapped as the entire cast came out for their curtain call. Bob stood beside Grumitch. The orchestra stood at their seats, the boys from the chorus were on one side of the stage and Bob's boys on the other. Doc Dowd jumped up on his seat looking for Rydell who came striding from the wings to center stage. "Perfect," he muttered. He aimed the remote at center stage and pushed the button.

A loud bang, followed by another and another and another. The cast stood back startled, and the audience applauded more and more at the fabulous finale. Bang, pop, pop, boom, bang went the cherry bombs one after another.

"You're the man!" said the man next to Dowd who had watched him push the button on the remote.

"What?" said Doc. "This was suppose to . . ."

"You Devon guys are terrific," he said slapping Doc on the back. "What a finish."

Mr. Ronciglione, thinking this was planned and that no one told him, turned to the orchestra and yelled, "Stars!" And the orchestra broke into *The Stars and Stripes Forever* as the cherry bombs continued to pop, bang, bang, boom.

Rydell shouted to Bob, "This your idea?"

"Not mine. I haven't a clue," he said over the explosions.

"Well, it's great."

The boys and the audience clapped in tempo to the orchestra. Bob looked up at Sandy who was grinning and clapping along with everyone else.

Forty-five explosions. Doc Dowd had wired them in a series instead of together.

"I have to get back to the school. Excuse me," he said pushing past the man.

The man stepped back. "You should be up there taking a bow," he said.

Crawfords tavern was crowded, and as soon as Bob and Sandy walked in folks cheered and applauded. Gladys ran over to Bob, gave him a big hug, "You were sensational, the whole program was sensational. Grumitch. Is he a trip or what? Looked just like him. And the boys, the speeches, the music, oh, and you and that little red wagon. Oh, Bob, I'm so proud of you. And that finale. Who on earth thought of that?"

Bob shrugged at the question, but thoroughly enjoyed the rush he was feeling. Sandy, her arm in his, shared a part of that.

As the guests left Gladys said good night, and Jimmy closed the bar leaving Bob and Sandy in a booth beside each other, their bodies touching comfortably.

" Was it David who triggered the sandwich man idea?" asked Sandy.

"Yes," he chuckled. "Just popped into my head when I was preparing the speech." He took her hand in his.

"And how about *your* journey?" asked Sandy. Where are you taking *your* little red wagon this summer?"

He turned to her, smiling broadly. "You'll never guess where. Wales. I want to see Tintern Abbey . . . with you."

Summer

Headmaster Rydell was sailing in Buzzard's Bay, Cape Cod, in his Herreshoff. He liked its wide beam so he could stretch out his legs. There was just enough breeze to push the little craft along and allow its captain the luxury of reading the mail he'd picked up before shoving off. There was a letter from Bob Hathaway post marked, Cardiff, Wales. He put his arm over the tiller and tore open the envelope.

Dear Lawrence,

My fiancée and I are having a wonderful time in Wales. That's right, Sandy is my fiancée. I proposed in Tintern Abbey, a truly magical place.

We stayed at the Marriott in Cardiff and last evening drove to Burry Port to hear the male choir rehearse. The Welsh are passionate about their singing and hold national competitions. We were the only tourists in a large parish hall listening to 60 male voices rehearse. There were men from all walks of life, and discipline was strictly enforced. (No talking while rehearsing.)

We plan on going to Cawley Island off the west coast. A water taxi takes us to the island where Cistercian monks live. Then we'll drive up the coast to see the marvelous castles.

I'm so pleased our Chautauqua venture was successful. I have some ideas for future speaking activities. One is a competition with other secondary schools in the area. Sort of a Speak Out.

Sandy sends her best.

Sincerely,

Bob

Rydell stuffed the letter back into the envelope, grabbed the tiller and sailed eastward along the curve in Cape Cod. The sail billowed as he let out the sheet. It was mid afternoon, and, as the little boat cut through the dark blue water, its contented captain fell into a sunny reverie of the year's accomplishments.

David Viraldi sat at a table in Chanticleer's kitchen creating the menus for the staff and readying his order for the food suppliers. Bob Hathaway was never far from his thoughts. Bob showed him his gift and validated what he was passionate about. He thought about that with every recipe he made, every salad he tossed, every sauce he simmered. "I should send him a picture of me in my cook's uniform," he said.

Teddy Garcia had his feet up on his uncle's cluttered desk in the office garage. He was reading American History, which was the extra course he would take in the fall to catch up with his class. Before he left school, Dr. Rydell gave him an early present. His Unclassified status was lifted. He became a full-fledged junior. He'd convinced the headmaster to let him add the History course to his schedule and promised to read the text over the summer to get a head start. The whirl of the window air conditioner fought the Florida humidity. A dehumidifier noisily drew the water from the air, but Teddy was engrossed with General Gage, Paul Revere and the Minute Men of Concord. He studied in the morning and helped his uncle in the afternoon.

He looked through the office window at his uncle in the hot garage, the sweat pouring off his face as he filed a piece of metal, a cigar clenched in his teeth. His uncle and mom teased about his voice changing. Seems overnight his boyish soprano was getting deeper, cracking now and then when he spoke, as his vocal chords lengthened. It pleased him but not nearly as much as the single whisker on his chin. He touched it frequently with his finger and searched for more. Not yet, but soon he knew.

Leon and Meredith Grumitch sat half way up the Dunne's River Falls in Ocho Rios, Jamaica, the water cascading on their shoulders. She dipped her cupped hand and trickled the water on her knee. Then she flicked some on Leon's face, and he slapped the water to splash her. The other tourists grinned at the child's play of two old folks. "I wonder where Bob and Sandy are now?" Meredith asked.

"Riding on cloud nine," he said leaning back into the falls. "He's quite a man that Hathaway."

"You didn't always think so," she said.

"True. I can't put my finger on when I changed my attitude toward him," he said leaning forward again. "He seems to bring out the best in people doesn't he?"

"He showed you a gift you didn't even know you had."

Leon nodded. He felt young again, vital and meaningful. Meredith looked at him lovingly. She saw the young man she fell in love with in an English class a long time ago. No longer an egocentric, academic curmudgeon, for that's what he'd become, but free now—proud and comfortable and confident and caring. She leaned over and kissed his forehead.

"What was that for?"

She just smiled and looked off to the bay. He reached out and touched her shoulder.

Doctor Timothy Dowd's plot was uncovered. The Devon Courier reviewed the performance as a news item. Seems the man that sat beside Doc was so impressed by the pyrotechnics, as he called them, that he bragged to everyone in town that he sat beside the man with the remote that set the whole thing off. When asked who the man was he didn't know, but he described him, and that's how Doc got his picture in the paper.

Doc was also singled out in West Hall in front of the entire student body and faculty for his ingenuity, and although Doc had no official part in the Evening of Chautauqua, Headmaster Rydell applauded his silent contribution that made the Chautauqua event spectacular. "Doc," he said, "you can eat soup with a one-tined fork, and Devon is honored to have you here. I hope you'll be with us for a long, long, time. As long as you want."

Timothy Dowd rose from the faculty section and walked up the aisle to shake Rydell's hand and receive the little plaque with his name engraved on it. When asked to speak, he softly said, "He moves in mysterious ways, listen for His voice." There was a delay in the applause for him, as everyone tried to figure out what that had to do with his getting an award, but, then, Doc was a little quirky, and they offered up their heartfelt applause.

Rydell made his final tack to the dock. He thought about Bob and Sandy and re-read their note. Tucking it back into his shirt pocket he said, "Society is full of headline seekers, but it's people like Bob Hathaway who carry on the everyday miracle of keeping our society a good society."

The Headmaster turned into the wind as he approached his slip. The sail fluttered, the boat slowed, bobbed and bumped the dock. He lowered the mainsail, secured it on the boom, and gathered his gear. He stepped onto the weather-beaten planks of the dock, tossed the duffel over his shoulder and headed up the hill to his cottage thinking of the line from Browning's *Pippa Passes.* "God's in his heaven, all's right with the world."

Appendix

How Bob Prepares a Speech

1. Once Bob's topic is decided, he draws a mind-map—a visual of all the things he knows and has experienced about the topic.

2. He talks aloud—a stream of consciousness—to see what happens as he covers the items on his mind-map. A legal pad is close at hand so he can jot down ideas and "good lines" as he shapes his speech.

3. A form evolves from this process. Opening sentence, point(s), stories, closing line. He writes the sequences down in his own form of shorthand.

4. Next Bob focuses on transitions from paragraph to paragraph. If he has trouble remembering what comes next, then he knows something is wrong with the transition and works on it, or throws it out because it obviously doesn't fit.

5. He analyzes the entire talk from the rough format he has made to be sure he is on target and that the speech has balance from story to story, point to point.

6. Now, he stands in his living room and delivers his speech to a pillow on his sofa—never taking his eyes off it. This tests his memory and forces him to focus on the exact speech he is going to deliver. (Some people talk to a stuffed animal or look at a spot on the wall.)

7. If he's going to use a story he has not delivered before, he will try it out in conversation with his friends to test their reaction and hone the economy of words.

8. He makes his final notes in the format you see in his Chautauqua speech. It is economical and entire 40 minute speech can be reviewed in less than a minute. He writes the notes over and over again as part of his rehearsal as well as rapidly speaking the heading of each segment of the speech. He locks it in.

9. The benefit of all this preparation allows him to enjoy the audience, relate to the people, and not have to worry about "what comes next?" in his presentation.

"Chautauqua" Notes

Bob Hathaway believes notes are only to help you with your sequence. This allows you to concentrate and connect with your audience. These are the notes he bought with him to the Opera House. Note how each story is bracketed.

<u>**How you relate to RW determines how you'll live your life.**</u>

RED WAGON POSITIONS

(Watson/Son) (Epitaph) (WSJ/Baby) (Luggage in RW)

HERO'S PATTERN

(King Arthur-Steps) (Student-Steps)

SANDWICH MAN

(Goal) (Reactions) (Bank) (Wise Woman)
(Action) (Policeman) (2 yrs later) (Store) (Fire)

SUPREME ORDEAL

(Knight---Student---Sandwich Man)

HERO AND RED WAGON

YOU ARE THE RED WAGON

<u>**Heroes eagerly fulfill the gift their Creator has given them.**</u>

Opening and closing sentences underlined. Bold Headlines. Stories in Brackets. While the sequences did not lend themselves to mnemonics, always look for them as a memory aid.

Articulation Excellence

The following 7 sounds will help stretch and strengthen the muscles of your mouth, lips, and tongue. Of all the sounds in the English language, these are the most beneficial for improved diction. Exaggerate each sound.

1. D, T, (duh, tuh): In "duh," tongue is firmly planted against the gum ridge behind the upper front teeth. You will feel the tip of your tongue flatten slightly. In "tuh", tongue is in the same area but narrowed. Start to pronounce "duh" and notice the firming of you throat muscles. Now, say "duh."
2. l (lllll): mouth open slightly, tongue narrowed against back of upper front teeth.
3. O (oh): purse lips forward and form an "O." Tongue is suspended in mouth.
4. P,B, (puh, buh): tighten lips hard against each other. Tongue suspended in mouth.
5. M (mmmm): tighten lips hard against each other and hold while saying "mmmmmmmmm."
6. N (nnnn): lips parted slightly, tongue at back of upper teeth flattened slightly against gum area above teeth.
7. R (rrrr): lips parted very slightly, tongue is spread against upper rear molars with center of tongue against roof of mouth.

Daily Practice (Exaggerate each word)

DOG DAY DOOM DO TOUCH TAG TODAY TIME

LITTLE LIL LEISURE LIE OH OKAY ONLY ONE

PUB PEN PIN PAY BUY BUYS BIG BAG MY

MINE MONEY MOM NO KNEEL NEED NOT

When speaking, be sure not to drop endings of words like: -ing, -ment, -ous, etc. Also, do not drop the final consonant of words.

Placement

The purpose of correct placement is to be easily and pleasantly understood and bring forth the true and unique sound of your voice. There are three areas where your voice can be placed: In the throat, through the nose, or in front of your face.

To hear/feel each of those sounds do the following.

To hear what your voice sounds like in your throat, try to talk making your voice as low as you possibly can. Chin on chest and the sound is buried in your throat.

To hear nasality, pinch your nose with your fingers and try to talk through it. Nasality sounds whiney.

Here's how to get your best vocal quality.

First, take a proper breath. Now, sing the vowels one at a time and picture them in front of your teeth.

Repeat, but this time smile as you sing the vowel.

This is called placing your voice forward. It enables you to use your entire face mask as a resonator; hence your true and best voice quality.

Telephone practice is good because there are no visual distractions. Listen to the other person, and I'll guarantee you'll be able to tell whether they are smiling or not. Smiling helps bring the voice forward. The result is clear and pleasant.

Picture your words in front of your face as you talk, and you'll be on your way to perfect placement.

The Ladder of Intangible Needs

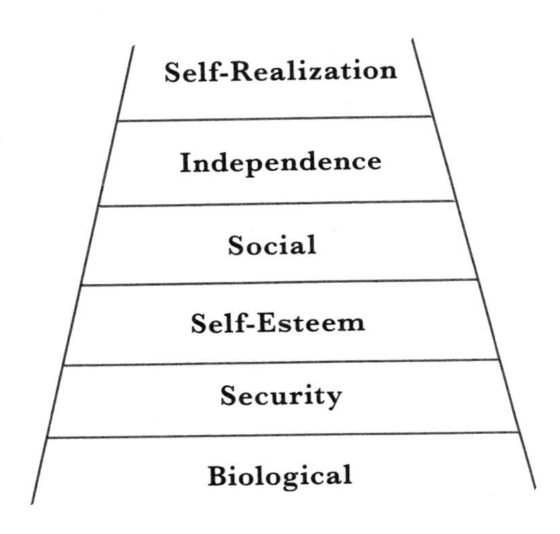

In *DEVON*, the ladder deviates from Psychologist Abraham Maslow's Hierarchy of Needs by adding the Independence need.

The author spoke (11/05/2004) with a former student of Maslow, Robert Lefton, Ph.D., co-founder of Psychological Associates. Dr. Lefton explained: dependence and independence are part of the growth cycle from childhood to the adult world; however, in the adult world Independence can take on two forms: Authoritative, bossy, "leave me alone, I'll do it myself" manifestation or, a mode of collaborative *inter*dependence.

Maslow felt Independence was part of the Self-Esteem and Self-Realization needs and not a separate entity on the ladder. Yet, when Dr. Lefton presented his former teacher with *his* definitions of independence as applied in the business world, Maslow agreed: Independence has a place in the hierarchy.

The author chose the "adapted" Lefton ladder because of his strong beliefs in the need to assess Independence when the occasion calls for a self-assessment in one's career. Questions might be: "Are you comfortable in your own skin?" Or, as Bob asked of David, "You were your own man weren't you?"

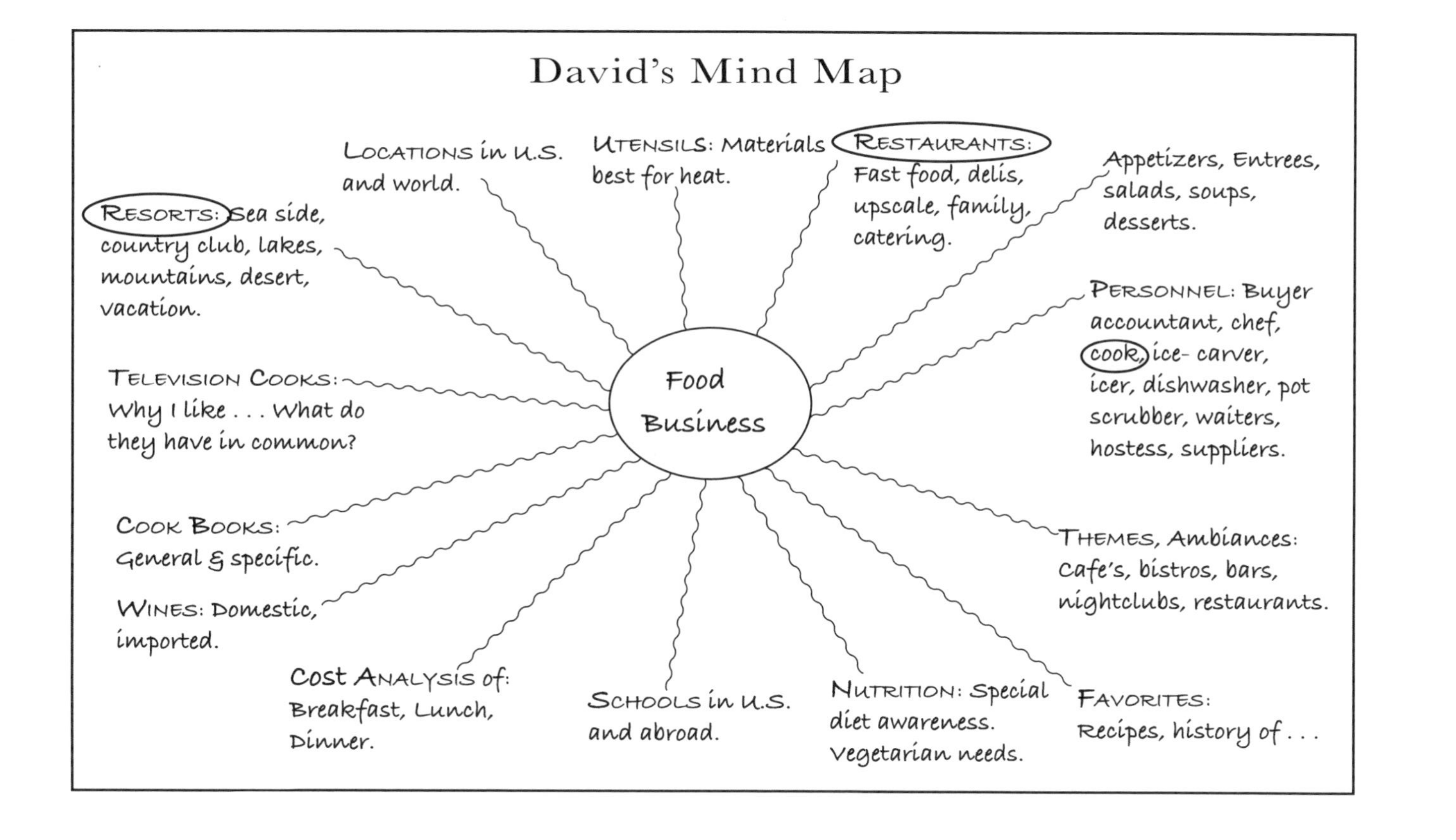
David's Mind Map
Food Business
RESORTS: Sea side, country club, lakes, mountains, desert, vacation.
LOCATIONS in U.S. and world.
UTENSILS: Materials best for heat.
RESTAURANTS: Fast food, delis, upscale, family, catering.
Appetizers, Entrees, salads, soups, desserts.
PERSONNEL: Buyer accountant, chef, cook, ice- carver, icer, dishwasher, pot scrubber, waiters, hostess, suppliers.
TELEVISION COOKS: Why I like . . . What do they have in common?
COOK BOOKS: General & specific.
WINES: Domestic, imported.
Cost ANALYSIS of: Breakfast, Lunch, Dinner.
SCHOOLS in U.S. and abroad.
NUTRITION: Special diet awareness. Vegetarian needs.
THEMES, Ambiances: Cafe's, bistros, bars, nightclubs, restaurants.
FAVORITES: Recipes, history of . . .

Recommended Reading

Baker, Carlos. *Ernest Hemingway, A Life Story.* New York: Charles Scribner's Sons, 1969. Leon Grumitch used this book to prepare for his portrayal at the Opera House. A thorough and insightful read for those who want to learn more about the man who's style has stood the test of time.

Brusaw, Charles T., Gerald J. Alred, Walter E. Oliu. *The Business Writer's Handbook, Seventh Edition.* New York: St. Martin's Press, 2003. Items are arranged alphabetically. This is an indispensable reference book. Succinct answers to your immediate questions make it easy to write accurately.

Case, Victoria, Robert Ormond Case. *We Called It Culture, The Story of Chautauqua.* New York: Doubleday & Company, Inc., 1948. This hard to find book will give you the thrill of "being there." It is written with all the passion and excitement of Chautauqua's audiences and performers. I suggest contacting Powells Books (www.powells.com) for help in finding a used copy.

Hoffman, Edward, *The Right To Be Human,* A biography of Abraham Maslow. Los Angeles, California: Jeremy P. Tarcher, Inc. 1988.

Hunt, Leigh (1784-1859) *Abou Ben Adhem.*

Lefton, Robert E., V.R. Buzzotta, *Leadership Through People Skills.* New York, New York: McGraw-Hill, 2004.

For information on mind-mapping, visit: *www.mind-map.com.*

The Great Connection Series

The acceptance of this series has been international. Mr. Warren's books have bridged cultural nuances in 11 languages and has brought a sound foundation in people skills to all.

• *The Great Connection* identifies your behavior style including your effective and ineffective traits. TGC explains how to determine the style of others and gives you the exact words to use to connect with them. *"The Great Connection has positively impacted my life both personally and professionally, as well as the lives of those I serve."*

• *Personal On-Line Assessment* for leaders, managers, team captains, and individuals in relationships. Go on-line now and get your 20+ page report, which includes not only a detailed description of your style but also 15 classic behavior patterns to help you recognize the styles of others—vital for effective communication with family and business associate. (www.greatconnection.com)

• The *Personal Action Guide* transcends the typical "workbook." This Guide elevates your ability to connect with others.

• *Find Your Passion* highlights three powerful steps to help you realize what you're good at so you can determine the career path meant for you. Researched with Edith Donohue, Ph.D., the methodology presented is solid, sound, proven.

• *The Great Connection Sequel: Devon* helps you write and speak with clarity and confidence. No more uncertainty as to where to put the comma; no more hesitancy before speeches. And like all of Mr. Warren's books, a delightful story.

About the Author

Arnie Warren's career has taken him from top morning radio personality in Miami to CBS Radio in St. Louis where he was recognized by *Radio and Records* as one of the nation's best interviewers. His voice is heard on books for the sight impaired in the Library of Congress.

He taught Speech at the University of Miami; TV Production in the Dade County Vocational System; and traveled extensively conducting seminars on behavioral styles and communication skills.

His first book, *The Great Connection*, has reached a world-wide audience. *"If you know who you are and what you're good at and understand basic communication skills, you can write your own ticket."*

The author lives in Florida with his wife, Kathleen. They share their home with Tyrus, a Siamese cat, and Louis, a Golden Retriever.

You may email Mr. Warren at: arniewarren@msn.com.